Printed Electronics and the Automatic Identification of Objects

An Investigation of the Emerging and Developing Technologies Related to the Generation Beyond Print-on-Paper

By Michael L. Kleper,
Paul and Louise Miller Distinguished Professor, School of Print Media, Rochester Institute of Technology

GATF*Press*

PITTSBURGH

International Standard Book Number: 0-88362-489-3
Printed in the United States of America
GATF Catalog No. 1748

Product names are mentioned in this report as a matter of
information only and do not imply endorsement by the
Graphic Arts Technical Foundation or Michael L. Kleper.

GATF*Press* books are widely used by companies, associations, and schools
for training, marketing, and resale. Quantity discounts are available by
contacting Peter Oresick at 800/910-GATF.

Graphic Arts Technical Foundation
200 Deer Run Road
Sewickley, PA 15143-2600
Phone: 412/741-6860
Fax: 412/741-2311
Internet: www.gain.net

Printing Industries of America
100 Daingerfield Road
Alexandria, VA 22314
Phone: 703/519-8100
Fax: 703/548-3227
Online: www.gain.net

Table of Contents

ABSTRACT

The purposes of this report are to:

- Communicate advances that are likely to enable the use of printing for the manufacture of electronic devices.

- Identify the materials and processes that will be used in the manufacture of printed electronics.

- Provide detailed information about intelligent documents and smart labels and the innovative uses of paper.

- Report on developments in the automatic identification of objects and the potential opportunities that may await the printing industry in the manufacture of components of Radio Frequency Identification (RFID) tags.

- Survey the field in regard to the implementation of an RFID infrastructure to support the consumer goods supply chain and the potential for printing all or part of an RFID tag.

The printing industry is about to enter a new age, one that may redefine, at least in part, its purpose and its product. Recent advances in material science now make it possible to use printing processes to produce electronic components and devices—with the potential to do so inexpensively and in great number. Printing, as a form of precise patterning, offers the greatest hope for enabling the "Internet of Things," a phase of technological evolution in which everyday objects in the environment incorporate some degree of intelligence.

Advances in Automated Identification & Data Capture (AIDC) technology are likely to impact its most ubiquitous form, the Universal Product Code, which is printed on almost every product label, package, and carton worldwide. Market demand, from large retailers such as Wal-Mart and large manufacturers such as Proctor and Gamble, is paving the way for the UPC's electronic counterpart: the Radio Frequency Identification (RFID) tag. The technology that will enable the deployment of RFID tags by the billions will likely be one or more forms of printing.

A survey conducted as a part of this report suggests that there is relatively little known about RFID in the label printing sector of the industry. Experts in RFID technology believe that RFID tags are likely to replace UPC in the next twenty years, and that printing is likely to play a major role in that process.

INTRODUCTION

It is becoming increasingly evident that the patterns in our environment, from DNA structures to device circuitry, can be replicated using various forms of printing. The printing process, if not the conventional printing press itself, is destined to launch a new age of information dissemination that is typified not by the printed page but by the mass production of printed electronic devices. This occurs, ironically, at a time when traditional printing of ink on paper is declining with the information instead being diverted to on-screen reading. In the report titled *The Generation Beyond Print-on-Paper* (PICRM-2002-01), information was presented regarding the growing use of computer monitors, and other forms of display, for the presentation of material that is either also available in print or composed exclusively for electronic display. Less print is being produced today, yet more data and information is generated. In the competition for readers, print is losing to electronic presentation. Ultimately, however, the printing process will enable the transfer, storage, and display of more information than ever before using inexpensive electronic reading devices and other forms of digital presentation and containment.

Print is certainly not headed for extinction. The use of print is a vital and important part of daily life and will continue to be so long after the printed characters that you are reading fade away or the electrons forming a display image decay into oblivion. The good news for print is that the very technology that has been eroding its market (that is, electronic displays) may potentially be produced in whole or in part using printing methods, in some cases by conventional printing presses. This, of course, would be the ultimate irony. Printing, as it has from the time of its invention, offers the possibility of producing mass quantities quickly and at low cost, and, as it did in the fifteenth century, it will bring a new form of literacy to the masses.

The use of the printing process for the fabrication of electronic components, such as displays, back planes, memory, antennas, batteries, etc., is possible because of advances in materials and fundamental research related to the formation of electronic circuits on thin, flexible plastic. Printing, like electronics fabrication, is a process that involves the accurate application of finely articulated patterns in precise repetition. It is an established technology that will enable a new and exciting future in which intelligence is incorporated into virtually everything that we come into contact with in our daily lives. This report includes information on some of the latest developments in display technology and introduces RFID technology, which is likely to revolutionize our lives.

In Europe a major initiative, named PolyApply, has been launched to begin what will certainly be the largest polymer[1] electronics research and development program in history. Now involving participants in North America and Asia, the goal is to advance the science associated with polymer circuitry to commercialize organic displays, RFID tags, memory, and other electronic components. The scope of the project is not only global but also broad based and is likely to include the participation of commercial printing companies. The European Union has made a substantial financial investment with the expectation that plastic-based circuit applications will be brought to market over the next ten years.[2]

Printing Is Patterning

The worlds of computer science and commercial printing have found common ground by virtue of the recognition that the minute traces that enable the creation of electronic circuits are patterns not unlike those used to print words and images. The work of Heeger, MacDiarmid, and Shirakawa, which earned them the 2000 Nobel Prize for Chemistry, showed that impurities could be added to plastics, through a process called *doping*, that would endow the plastic with conductive, semiconductive, and electroluminescent properties. Considerable work has been done to demonstrate that through a variety of "printing" processes it is possible to make displays and a wide variety of electronic components and devices.

Polymers, which are transparent, are already used in 95% of all electronics fabrication, from circuit-board coatings to adhesives. Interest in the development of low-cost, mass-produced pliable Integrated Plastic Circuit (IPC) chips, flexible displays, and thin-film batteries has given rise to a new industry, dubbed "polytronics" by the Fraunhofer Research Institute in Germany. Although polymer-based chips are over one hundred times slower than traditional silicon-based chips, the market for low-cost, disposable, single-purpose ICs is staggering. The mass production of cheap chips, through some form of roll-to-roll printing process, will enable a new age in which chips will be embedded in virtually everything. According to Fraunhofer, "Low-cost mass-production is only possible through print processes, not with the costly etching and electrostatic coating processes that are required in clean-room semiconductor manufacturing. Electronic circuits made from organic semiconductors are comparatively inexpensive and simple to produce. Because most polymers are soluble, the circuits can simply be printed. Circuit structures with a width in the 10- to 100-micrometer range can be produced in this way."[3]

Within the next ten years there will be a gradual shift from the manufacture of print to the use of print for manufacture—that is, from the application of print for reading materials to the application of printed patterns for the creation of electronic devices.

Although there is a primary concern over the size of features that can and will be printed for device manufacture, certain patterning methods, such as those proposed by Add-Vision (PICRM-2002-01, page 40), are not dependent upon fine feature imaging, but instead on the composition of the ink that is used to print light-emissive displays.

Printing has always been judged by what can be seen; it has always been evaluated by the human eye (See Table A: Units of Measurement and Their Comparative Application in Printing). An obvious example of this is the need for trapping, through the use of spreads and chokes. This purposeful overlapping of inked areas is necessary both because the human eye can see small differences, and will notice minute gaps between colors, and because the variables in the printing process, in the materials, and in the press itself have inherent flaws that can cause one printed sheet to differ from another.

Method

The proliferation of digitally delivered information has often been at the expense of traditional print. Digital delivery to the information end-user typically results in the display of the information, rather than the information taking a printed form.[5] This research looks at recent developments in display technology and the opportunities for the application of conventional printing technology as a method not only of producing displays and their associated components but also electronic devices of all kinds. This paper is based on an exhaustive literature search (see References), interviews, and correspondence with key industry players, attendance at several industry seminars and events,[6] and an industry survey to assess the possible application of traditional printing methods for the production of RFID tags, which are the likely successors to printed UPC bar codes and one of the first opportunities for large-scale printing of electronic components.

The Automatic Identification of Objects

Virtually every manufactured item in our environment has a label or some other form of identification. These labels are printed and provide valuable, often vital, information concerning the contents, use, manufacturer or source, and often various kinds of descriptive data. Recent advances in polymer electronics and conductive inks are likely to enable the printing of remote-sensible labels that may lead to significant improvements and monumental changes in the methods and processes by

Unit	Abbr.	Fraction of m/in.	Scientific Notation	Inch Equivalent
inch	in	1 inch		1.0
centimeter	cm	1/100 of a meter	1×10^{-2}	2.54
millimeter	mm	1/1,000 of a meter	1×10^{-3}	25.4
mil	mil	1/1,000 of an inch		1000
micrometer or micron	µm	1/1,000,000 of a meter	1×10^{-6}	25,400
nanometer	nm	1/1,000,000,000 of a meter	1×10^{-9}	25,400,000
angstrom	å	1/10,000,000,000 of a meter	1×10^{-10}	254,000,000

Table A. Units of measurement and their comparative application in printing.

Comparative Measure	Printed Feature Dimensions	Printable Features
"It is ordained that 3 grains of barley, dry and round, make an inch..." (13th Century English law) *Commonly measured as the distance between the first and second joints of the human hand.*		
A human hair is approx. 3 mils wide. *The human eye can resolve two hairs, separated by the width of one hair, at 10 inches.*	*The width of a UPC line at 12 points is approx. 8 mil.*	*Conductive litho inks can print line resolutions of 1 mil (25 microns). Flexo/gravure conductive inks can print line resolutions of 2 mil (50 microns).[4]*
Diameter of a human hair = 20–60 μm. *Diameter of paper fibers are approx. 12 μm.* *Size of finest printable feature is about 20 μm.*	*Intel transistor size was 10 microns in 1971. Today Bell Labs stamping technology supports features as small as 0.2 micron on glass, plastics, metals, etc. in lab experiments.*	
Human hair is 50,000 to 100,000 nanometers in width.	*Today, Extreme Ultraviolet Lithography (EUVL) produces 157-nm transistors and logic gates. IBM has fabricated 90-nm transistors. Princeton and Stanford researchers are working on 10-nm transistors; however its applications in manufacturing are predicted, by Taiwan Semiconductor's director of Brand Management, Chuck Byers, to be twenty-five years away.*	

which objects are identified automatically. These developments are likely to have a profound and lasting impact on the printing industry.

The need for object identification is obvious. In the United States the average retailer experiences a "shrinkage" of their inventory of about 2% annually due to shoplifting, employee theft, supplier fraud, and administrative mistakes. That is compounded by an estimated 4% of sales that are lost when customers cannot find items that they want to purchase on a retailer's shelf, either because the items are out of stock or they have not been replenished from the stockroom. Both of these problems can be reduced, if not eliminated, using automatic identification of goods. In addition, it is speculated that a complete closed-loop supply chain solution can enable a retailer to operate more efficiently with a reduced inventory.[7]

The earliest work on the mechanical tracking of consumer goods (that is, Auto-ID[8]) was done in 1932 at the Harvard University Graduate School of Business Administration. Wallace Flint, the son of a Massachusetts grocery wholesaler, produced a thesis in partnership with a group of classmates. They devised a method of mechanizing consumer purchasing by having customers select merchandise from a catalog and remove the punched card that was associated with each item. The punched cards were given to a person designated as the "checker," who fed them into a card reader. The reader was connected to conveyer belts that delivered products automatically to customers. A customer bill was generated and the inventory system was adjusted accordingly. The system failed due to its complexity and expense, although it was a model for what was to come. Forty years later, Flint, as the vice president of the National Association of Food Chains, became a proponent of the then emerging bar code standard.

Bar codes as we know them today (Figure 1) can be traced to the work of Norman Joseph Woodland, a graduate student and teacher at Philadelphia's Drexel Institute of Technology. In 1949 he had a conversation with Bernard Silver, a Drexel student who had overheard a discussion between a Drexel dean and the president of a chain of grocery markets. The food store president wanted the university to do research on how information could be gathered automatically during checkout. The problem confronting supermarkets, he explained, was daunting. They carried thousands of items, many in a variety of sizes and variations, and most with relatively small mark-ups. The only way that a store could know at any point in time what was on their shelves was to close down and count every item. Despite his plea, the dean turned down his request.

Figure 1. The UPC symbol as produced in the 1975 IBM Systems Journal (Volume 14, Number 1) report by D. Savir and G.J. Laurer. (Reprint of the report provided through the courtesy of G.J. Laurer.)

Woodland was fascinated by the challenge, and one day while sitting on the beach it occurred to him that Morse Code might be the solution since it provided a simple yet sophisticated graphic representation of information. As he made dots and dashes in the sand and lengthened each symbol downward with his finger, he formed thin lines from dots and thick lines from the dashes, forming the first two-dimensional bar code. All bar codes are simply patterns of lines and spaces.[9]

Silver and Woodland devised the first bar codes in the shape of a bull's-eye, resembling in some respects the shape of the concentric rings on an LP record. Its advantage was that it could be read from any direction, eliminating the need to orient the bar code in reference to the reader. They also devised a straight line pattern similar to what is used today. They received a patent for their technology in 1952, which they sold to Philco in 1962, and which Philco sold to RCA in 1971. The technology, however, was in need of significant refinement for general use. In one of their bar code systems the reader consisted of a modified movie sound system, which had been invented in the 1920s by Lee de Forest. The hardware was bulky, expensive, and required high-wattage bulbs which proved to be unsafe. In another system they printed the bar codes using ink which glowed under ultraviolet light. Although the device worked, the ink was not sufficiently stable, and the process of printing the bar codes was excessively expensive. Today, of course, the cost of printing the bar code is negligible.

In response to bar code developments at Sylvania and RCA, IBM, where Norman Woodland was employed, supported his research, which resulted in his development of what would become the Universal Product Code (UPC). The design of the UPC symbol was created by George J. Laurer at IBM, and he is considered the inventor of the ubiquitous code that is carried on virtually every consumer product in the world.[10]

The first commercial use of an auto-identification system in a supermarket was in a Kroger store in Cincinnati, OH, in 1972. That short-lived system, made by RCA, used a bull's-eye code design which was printed on separate labels which were applied by hand by the Kroger employees. This site was plagued by errors caused by poorly printed symbols, which tended to smear in the direction that the paper had moved through the press. The advantage of the UPC symbol design, consisting of straight lines, was that it was not affected by excessive ink. Any excess ink would be drawn up in the direction of the lines. The pervasiveness of the UPC bar code forced printers to learn how to reproduce it accurately and reliably.[11]

The Kroger experiment was followed a year later by acceptance of the UPC symbology as the industry standard. IBM introduced it on April 3, 1973, with the use of readers from NCR.[12] The first purchase of a bar-coded item was at 8:01 A.M. on June 26, 1974, at Marsh's Supermarket in Troy, OH. The item, a ten-pack of Wrigley's Juicy Fruit Gum is on display at the Smithsonian Institute's National Museum of American History (Figure 2). The item was randomly lifted from the shopper's cart and passed into the annals of auto-ID history.[13]

The bar-code symbology was a significant scientific breakthrough, but it required the invention of inexpensive lasers and integrated circuits to make the system economically feasible. By the late 1970s more than 85% of all products had a printed code, yet in 1978 less than 1% of all grocery stores had the equipment to read them. That number climbed to 10% by mid-1981, to 33% by mid-1984, and to more than 60% by the end of 2002.[14]

Despite the relatively low-tech nature of bar codes, new applications continue to be developed. These include such diverse uses as attaching tiny bar codes to bees to track their mating habits and to the army's use of two-foot-long bar codes to label boats stored at West Point. The Uniform Code Council continues to define new standards, such as the Reduced Space Symbology (RSS) for labeling produce and particularly small items and the 2005 Sunrise initiative that supports implementation of the twelve-digit UPC symbol by January 1, 2005.

A variety of bar code symbolisms have been developed to address particular applications and to embody particular features. The arrangement of lines and spaces have been specified to represent character sets that serve the needs of specific industries. For example, the Universal Product Code is used primarily in the retail and grocery industry to mark items for sale to consumers;

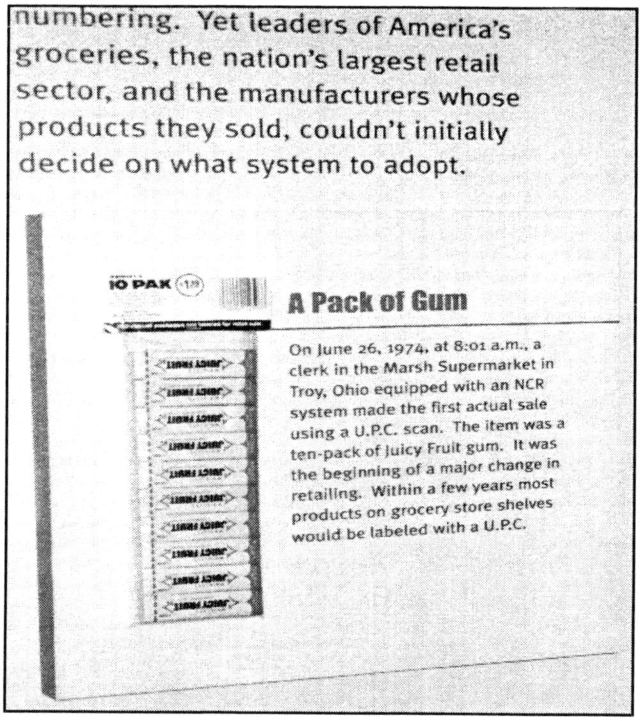

numbering. Yet leaders of America's groceries, the nation's largest retail sector, and the manufacturers whose products they sold, couldn't initially decide on what system to adopt.

A Pack of Gum

On June 26, 1974, at 8:01 a.m., a clerk in the Marsh Supermarket in Troy, Ohio equipped with an NCR system made the first actual sale using a U.P.C. scan. The item was a ten-pack of Juicy Fruit gum. It was the beginning of a major change in retailing. Within a few years most products on grocery store shelves would be labeled with a U.P.C.

Figure 2. The first bar-coded item to be scanned was a multi-pack of Wrigley's Juicy Fruit Gum. That package is on display at the Smithsonian in Washington, D.C. (Photo courtesy of George J. Laurer, inventor of the UPC bar code.)

1 2 3 4 5 6 7 8 9 0

A

Prof. Michael Kleper
Rochester Institute of Technology
School of Print Media
69 Lomb Memorial Drive
Rochester, NY 14623

B

Figure 3. (A) The Code 39 symbology. (B) The Post NET symbology.

Code 39 is used in manufacturing for inventory and industrial applications,[15] and Post NET is used for encoding U.S. Postal Service Zip Codes (Figure 3). Prior to the universal acceptance of these symbolisms, each company used its own system to mark its products. This free-market method resulted in great variation and produced marked goods that could not easily be deciphered by anyone other than their manufacturer. The acceptance of bar-coding standards required all manufacturers to register with the Uniform Code Council (UCC).[16]

Alan Haberman, who chaired the subcommittee in 1971 that accepted the black-and-white bar code that is still in use, states that the grocery industry realized annual cost reductions of about $17 billion in 1997 by virtue of the UPC as assessed from every part of the value chain, beginning with the manufacturing and packaging and ending at the check-out counter.[17]

Printing UPC Bar Codes

After the technical testing of the UPC bar code it became apparent that the next hurdle was integrating it within the design of package labels. The size of the bar code was dependent primarily upon the capabilities of the printing process, as well as the particular press used. According to George Laurer, a pioneer in the development of UPC technology, "there was a lot of work done with regard to printing the symbol before and after the choice was made in 1973. One of the overriding objectives of the symbol design was to design a code and symbol that could be printed using all the printing processes of the day. That of course included litho, rotogravure, and so on. Some presses were high speed, brand new in the seventies and some like the ones printing Maxwell House coffee cans in Hoboken, NJ were built during WWI."[18]

A commissioned study was conducted in the early 1970s by IBM in Rochester, MN, concerning the composition of the UPC bar code appearance. Rather than print an actual bar code of any type, the researchers scanned and analyzed the letter T from thousands of previously printed labels. The letter T appeared in the word *net weight*, which was already a part of virtually every extant label and was always printed relatively small. In addition, the letter had the advantage of being composed of two bars at right angles, so that no matter how it was printed, one of the bars would always be printed in the rotation direction of the press cylinder, and the other would be crosswise.

The results of the IBM study showed that the bar code would need to be constructed of linear elements and that a curvilinear design would not work. The bar width was specified as ±004-in. Since not all printing processes could maintain that degree of tolerance, the proposed standard was amended to allow for printing the bar code between 2× magnification, which would require four times the label area, and 0.8× magnification, which would require two-thirds of the nominal area, which was 1.5 square inch.

The only reasonable way for the UPC bar code to become a part of consumer goods was for the manufacturer to print them on the label, in other words, *sourcemark* them. Despite all of the positive reasons for implementing the UPC, there was resistance from manufacturers who did not want to give up any of their label real estate for an unattractive machine-readable bar code, from printers who were unfamiliar with the requirements yet concerned about the additional quality control it entailed, and from the grocers who would have to invest heavily in scanners and infrastructure and retrain their employees. Despite these hurdles, the UPC specification was finalized, and printers learned how to print reliable bar codes.[19]

Part of the package of UPC specification materials that printers received was a "printability gauge," which was a piece of film that printers could use to make test plates to determine their individual process capabilities. The film consisted of sets of bars positioned at right angles to each other, reminiscent of the "T" test conducted by IBM. According to George Laurer:

There were various densities or spacing and the groups were labeled E, F, H, and so on. Before committing to a major change in the label artwork, many printers, grocery converters, and label makers printed this gauge on the labels where it would be hidden or be inconspicuous on the finished package. Some even did this before the final symbol selection was made and included various symbols that were proposed. A chart which correlated the results of the printability gauge with the recommended magnification and print direction was provided with the specification. The specifications also included sections on inks, reflectivity, and imperfections. The specifications did not include a specification for the finished printed symbol. The specification was written in a way, that, if it were followed, the result would be an acceptable symbol. This was done because no one wanted a grocer to be able to reject a product because of a symbol that did not scan properly. One can imagine the problems if for example, 100 cases of peas were rejected because the symbol did not scan well or for some other reason associated with the symbol and not the product. As soon as the symbol specifications were released, the UCC[20] set up a number of *Symbol Technical Advisory Committees*. STAC-3 dealt with scanning and STAC-4 dealt with in-store printing of the symbol. Others dealt with symbol placement, film masters, packaging, and more. STAC-3 was most important since it was comprised mostly of scanning experts and thus handled most of the printing problems and/or questions. Printers used these forums to discuss their problems and learn how to print acceptable symbols.[21]

Although UPC bar codes have revolutionized tracking of consumer packaged goods (CPG) and other items, and approximately 5 billion of them are scanned everyday worldwide,[22] the coding technology has inherent limitations. Bar codes are read-only and contain a limited amount of general information relating only to the manufacturer and the product. In order for a bar code, which is not easily human readable or translatable, to be identified, it must be scanned by an electronic reader. Generally, the item must be handled, and the bar code must be positioned so that it can be scanned. The bar code must be visible, of course, and free of any imperfections, such as tears, torn or missing stripes, or dirt or disruptive markings. An item cannot be tallied in inventory until it has been scanned, and it must be scanned in some fashion as it moves through the supply chain and ultimately gets scanned in a checkout line. Items are scanned several times, either by *macro-scanning* them as part of cartons or *micro-scanning* them as individual goods.

Why RFID Will Replace UPC

The use of radio frequencies, rather than light, for automatic identification goes back more than fifty years. The earliest uses of automatic ID devices using radio frequency were during WWII, in the military, for transponder systems aboard aircraft to determine the "friend or foe" status (IFF, Identify Friend or Foe) of other planes.[23] It developed in the 1960s in crude forms for electronic article surveillance (EAS), using simple one-bit systems that merely sensed the presence or absence of the tag.

Radio Frequency Identification (RFID) tags as we know them today were invented by Mario Cardullo, who received the first patent (#3,713,148) for a passive, read-write RFID tag on January 23, 1973. Cardullo's idea for the technology came from a chance meeting that he had with an IBM engineer during a flight from Washington to St. Paul. The engineer was working on a system to track railroad cars called the CARTRAK Optical System. The system used an optical base station that transmitted a beam of light at a reflective color bar code adhered to the side of each railroad car. As the cars passed the reader, their identities were recorded. There were several problems with the system, which Cardullo could see would make the system unacceptable. The reading process would ultimately suffer from bar codes that could not be read due to dirt, mud, or other obstructions or from damage, alteration, or vandalism. According to Cardullo, "After the IBM engineer finished talking, I started to sketch in my notebook the idea for the RFID tag with a changeable memory. The original sketch showed a device with a transmitter, receiver, internal memory, and a power source. I signed and dated the sketch and went back to reading a book I had started."[24]

An RFID tag is, most generally, a small flat label that contains miniature electronics that can communicate information about the item of which it is a part. It has been described as "a disposable, wirelessly networked microcomputer."[25] Unlike UPC bar codes, an RFID tag does not need to be in the line of sight of the reader to be interrogated, can be read from a distance, and can in some cases store a significant amount of data. RFID tags are significantly more complex than UPC codes, which makes them more difficult and costly to produce and significantly more difficult to counterfeit, which is yet another benefit.[26] Despite the compelling case for RFID tags, it is predicted that even by 2015, less than 10% of the worldwide use of UPC bar codes will have been replaced with RFID tags.[27] For many years RFID tags and UPC bar codes will coexist and are likely to cohabitate products. Tag costs will need to drop significantly before their use will move from tagging pallets, to tagging cartons, to tagging individual goods. While highly sophisticated RFID tags cost over $100 each, IDTechEX, an RFID consultancy, states that "…a tag price below one cent (say 0.1 to 1 cent) will be needed to replace most bar codes, though markets of hundreds of billions of tags yearly will probably emerge at a tag price of one cent."[28]

It is not only the cost of tags that is holding back the widespread implementation of RFID technology, it is the cost of the scanners as well. Today scanners can cost several thousand dollars each, significantly more than those used for UPC scanning. The goal is to have scanners available for under $100 each. This pursuit is being followed by an MIT Media Lab spin-off company named ThingMagic.[29] Despite the cost issues, which are likely to be resolved in the near future, RFID has several advantages over UPC bar codes:

- RFID tags do not need to be in the reader's line of sight to be recognized.

- Several RFID tags can be read simultaneously.

- RFID tags can be read through walls and other obstructions. They are not affected by dirt, grease, paint, snow, mud, or other substances that might obscure their presence, i.e., they can be in rugged, unfriendly environments.

- RFID tags can be placed inside packaging or as a part of the product itself.

- RFID tags can maintain a significant amount of data about the item they identify.

- RFID tags can acquire data as the tagged item moves through the supply chain and beyond.

- Certain kinds of RFID tag can be erased and reused, thereby changing the item information it identifies.

- RFID tags can "talk" to other devices, such as a packaged meal communicating with a microwave oven in order to set cooking directions.

The application of an RFID tag to a product can enable the tracking of that product from its place of manufacture through the entire supply chain and into the home (see Table B. Some Examples of the Ultimate Market Potential for Total Asset Visibility with Peak Yearly Numbers of RFID Tags and Interrogators [Readers]). RFID tags are virtually 100% reliable and are considered the best form of automatic identification. Tags will make manufacturing plant, wholesale warehouse, and retail store inventories visible and manageable in real-time. Inventories will self-report, rather than need to be counted, and as a consequence will eliminate much of the product shrinkage that occurs from theft, loss, miscounts, and waste. Eventually, most items in the real world will contain tags and will enable a redefinition of the words *network* and *communication*.

RFID Tag Construction

Chip-based RFID tags generally consist of three components that work together to form a complete tag system, which is held on a supporting substrate (Figure 4). First is the silicon microprocessor, which stores information regarding the item that it is to identify. The data structure follows a scheme defined by the MIT Auto-ID Center.

Application	Peak Yearly Number M		Additional Challenges
	Tags	Interrogators	
Consumer Packaged Goods (CPG) Supply Chain	10,000,000 or more	20	Massive data processing, deliberate and accidental shielding, e.g., by water, reading discarded and spurious tags, tag removal, environmental concerns (not biodegradable, sometimes poisonous metals near food). Inadequate chip production capacity, wide geographical deployment.
Archiving including libraries, art galleries, museums, industrial plus assets in offices, factories, homes, etc.	1,000,000	10	Very large number of independent decision makers, widely dispersed. Many smallish applications.
Postal/Courier	650,000	1	Wide geographical deployment, electrical interference, security.
Other retail and business supply chains including health-care and military.	400,000	1	Fragmented market, widely dispersed. Security. Electrical interference with sensitive equipment. Very large number of independent decision makers, widely dispersed. Many smallish applications.
Vehicles, conveyances, air baggage, expensive products.	50,000	10	High speed. Security. Causing electrical interference with sensitive equipment.

Table B. Some examples of the ultimate market potential for total asset visibility with peak yearly numbers of RFID tags and interrogators (readers). Source: IDTechEx. Used with permission.

Second is the antenna, which may be a metal coil, an etched metal foil, or may be printed using a conductive ink. If an ink is used, the antenna is printed on paper, polyester, polyimide, ABS, PVC, or polycarbonate. Passive RFID tags do not contain a power source. They receive magnetic energy generated by the tag reader through their antennas. The energy is modulated by the chip and transmitted or "backscattered" back to the reader, similar to the way that light is reflected back from a distortion mirror; in this case, the reader sends the light, and the tag reflects it back modified by the tag's content. The third element is the material which the chip and antenna are attached to or enclosed in.[30]

Passive RFID tags do not contain a power source and therefore must be energized by the reader. To enable this the tag requires very high radio signal levels that are approximately 1000 times those used in active RFID systems.

Most RFID tag designs do not support cancellation. Tags remain detectable throughout their life, despite the fact that there are good reasons for killing a tag after it has served its purpose. Conversely, certain tag applications, such as proof of item ownership or tracing an animal, require that the tag is always detectable.

Passive tags are relatively inexpensive, and due to their lack of a self-contained power source, their shelf life is almost limitless. Both passive and active tags can be categorized into three groups:

- **Read Only:** These are the least complex of the tag types. Their identities are embedded into the tag during manufacture.

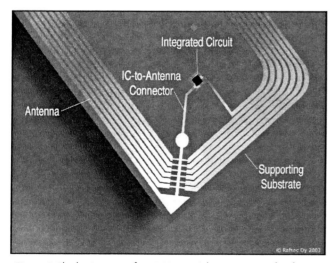

Figure 4. The basic parts of an RFID tag. (Photo courtesy of Rafsec.)

- **Write Once, Read Many (WORM):** These tags can be written just once and that data cannot be altered thereafter.

- **Read-Write:** This type of tag is usually the most expensive since data must be stored and retrieved.

Sophisticated RFID chips can store a significant amount of data—up to seventy pages.[31] Even a limited amount of data, consisting simply of a manufacturer code and model number, can yield extensive data from an online computer system, as proposed by the MIT Auto-ID Center.

RFID Infrastructure

An RFID tag in its simplest form, that is, a passive tag, is read-only and contains only the basic information required to identify it. It is derisively referred to as a "license plate" because it serves only the basic function of identifying an item, just as a license plate is linked to a record of data associated with a particular car. Despite limited capabilities, passive RFID tags are the likely successor to UPC bar codes. RFID tags which incorporate a silicon chip or Surface Acoustic Wave (SAW) technology can exhibit a range of up to 10 meters (32.81 feet).

RFID-tagged items are identified using an Electronic Product Code, or "EPC."[32] The Auto-ID Center has specified 96 bits of storage to contain the code, although in the future it may be expanded to 256 bits. The 96 bits of storage can support the unique identification of more than 268 million manufacturers, each having in excess of one million products, and still not exhaust the supply of numbers for years to come. The amount of content carried by the code, multiplied by the number of items that will contain it, is, however, presently beyond the capacity that any database can manage.[33]

The EPC contains a relatively small amount of data, which is good since it requires only modest read-only memory in the IC chip. The four fields contained in the EPC hold the following information:

- the version number of the EPC
- the manufacturer number
- the product number
- the unique tag serial number.

Tagged items are interrogated using wireless radio frequency readers which are strategically placed in the supply chain, from the point of manufacture to the point of purchase or use. The readers can accurately sense the EPC code that has been stored in the RFID tag. They send that data to the Internet where detailed information about that item is stored. The information regarding any object or item is located using an Object Naming Service (ONS), which is similar to the Domain Name System (DNS), which locates particular computers on the Internet on the basis of their URL. As a tag is scanned, its EPC code will be read, interpreted by Savant middleware (Java), and sent to the ONS where the data will be interpreted. The ONS will be magnitudes of size larger than DNS since it will need to locate data on literally trillions of objects. The physical objects that the ONS locates will be described using a new language, called the Product Markup Language (PML) (see Figure 5).

The sale of RFID-tagged items will provide the retailer with the potential to capture significant information about the buyer. In order to benefit from that data, retailers will need to have conduits between their inventory and accounting systems and their customer relationship management (CRM) software. In addition it will be necessary that tags and scanning equipment are standardized so that any tag can be read by any scanner.

An RFID tag has the potential to be much more than an identification label. Technology can be applied to extend the functionality to include sophisticated sensing and other advanced capabilities such as:

• The generation of sound as simple as a tone or as complex as music or speech. The sound could be triggered as an alarm or to direct attention toward an item to entice a sale. Voice instructions might be incorporated to augment printed package directions.

• The storage of short duration speech. Speech could be recorded on the label to provide individualized package instructions, such as prescription directions for a particular patient. Assistive "talking"

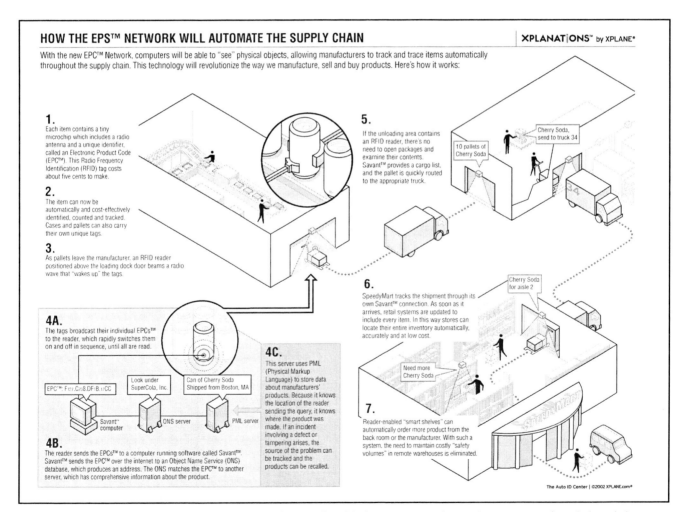

Figure 5. The application of RFID tags at the point of manufacture will enable the automatic tracking and management of goods through the supply chain. (Image used with the permission of the MIT Auto-ID Center.)

systems for medication dispensing for the blind are already in use.

- The addition of a self-modifying element of the label. A portion of the label might change color or display a modified expiration date (longer or shorter) in response to temperature changes or transportation conditions that have occurred during transit and storage.

- The use of a moving package-bound display. The label may contain a display with active elements, such as a blinking word, animated type, or motion video.

- The incorporation of data that can be electronically interrogated. Using a PDA or cell phone a shopper might be able to locate a specific item by name, ingredients, price, or other attribute.

The Economic Benefits and Burden

The benefits of applying RFID technology have been shown in case after case, where their use has provided positive, measurable results in product and asset tracking, loss prevention and reduction, inventory management, distribution efficiency, customer response, product turnover, spoilage reduction, access control, supply chain integrity, and more. Significant barriers to adoption exist due to the relatively high-cost tags and the support infrastructure to read and process them (see Table C. Global Market for RFID Smart Labels and Systems—2003 to 2015). Manufacturers have not agreed on standards, and it may be years before the price of readers reaches that of those used for UPC. The widespread implementation of RFID has been stalled by several factors, including:

- A lack of worldwide standards for tag designs, frequencies, and readers. Even today tags designed for a particular reader cannot universally be read with readers from competing manufacturers.

- A lack of a standard infrastructure for RFID tag use that will allow for flexible implementations that can meet any manufacturing, warehousing, and retailing situation.

- A debate over who in the supply chain will bear the added cost of providing an RFID tag to products, changing workflows and supply chain practices, and renovating buildings and vehicles with readers and other equipment.

- A consideration of the full costs of implementing a comprehensive RFID system, which for every node along the supply chain consists of investments in equipment, the IT infrastructure, and training.

- A recognition that implementation will require billions, likely trillions, of tags. It is estimated that at any point in time, Kimberly Clark, for example, has 10 billion units in the supply chain, and Unilever has 20 billion units.[34]

- The production of a truly low-cost (sub-one cent) RFID tag. The 5-cent tag proposed by the Auto-ID Center assumes that the chip price is 1 to 2 cents, which necessitates that the size of the silicon used for each IC would be about 0.25 mm^2.[35]

- The need for scaling operations to size. The volume of RFID tags that will be necessary to support a widespread supply chain infrastructure will be unprecedented. Manufacturing processes will require high-speed roll-to-roll equipment incorporating robotic assembly and testing. The Auto-ID Center speculates that the testing and application process would work like this: "the tags can arrive at

	2003	2005	2010	2015
Tag Value—$ millions	528	1,480	4,800	10,000
Number—millions	975	6,325	80,000	1,000,000
Unit price—cents	54.1	23.3	6.0	1.0
% TAV* by value—$ millions	5	10	50	70
Infrastructure and services value—$ millions	472	1,520	5,200	14,000
* Total Asset Visibility				

Table C. Global market for RFID Smart Labels and systems—2003 to 2015. Source: IDTechEx. Used with permission.

the facility on rolls with adhesives on the back; prior to application, a tag can be singulated and the EPC written to it; the tag can then be tested, and discarded if it is faulty; and finally, if the tag works, it can be applied to the package."[36]

- The lack of adequate capacity. It is estimated by the Auto-ID Center that if every integrated circuit fabrication facility in the world were to be diverted to RFID tag manufacture they could, at best, produce between 3–4 billion tags per day. This is 2–3 billion short of the number of UPC bar codes that are scanned daily.

Active RFID Tags

RFID tags that contain a low-cost disposable battery are called Smart Active Labels, or SAL. These tags, by virtue of their stored energy system, have a range of up to 100 meters (328.08 feet) and can store data, such as the date and time of manufacture and the time/date stamps for each movement through the supply channel. Active RFID tags are optimally produced at the 433 MHz frequency and provide a wavelength of about one meter. The largest Active RFID implementation in the world uses the 433 MHz frequency at hundreds of sites in more than twenty countries to track daily shipments conveyed over water, in the air, on the rails, and on highways. High-speed monitoring of large moving objects, like railroad cars, is done using 2.45 GHz to 5.8 GHz. Philips Electronics estimates their volume of smart labels at over 50 million per year for 2002, growing to two billion by 2004.[37]

Active RFID tags have some advantages over Passive tag technology. An Active tag can initiate communication and can engage in "conversations" of greater duration and containing more data. Their on-board energy source gives them the capability to persevere, even in environments in which data transmission is problematic. They are more complex, so they can communicate more and store more. On the other hand, their energy sources can deplete, and when that happens, they cease to function until a fresh power supply is provided.

Active RFID tags incorporate an energy source, which makes them more expensive than passive tags. Passive tags, however, may use a self-contained power supply, not to extend their range but to back up memory and facilitate data handling. These tags are classified as *semi-passive* RFID tags.

RFID Tag Frequencies

RFID tags respond to signals that are generated by readers, also called "interrogators." The readers generate signals at a particular frequency that the tag can respond to. Tags are therefore also known as *transponders*. Although tags do not need to be in the line of sight of the reader, as is the case for UPC bar codes, the path between tag and reader can not be blocked by water, which will absorb radio waves, or metal, which can reflect them. On the other hand, tags can be reliably read through up to two inches of non-metallic materials, including plastic, wood, cloth, and concrete.

A reader not only transmits a signal that the tag can respond to, it also receives the returned signal. Since it both transmits and receives it is a *transceiver*.

Issues exist with the problem of *signal collisions* that result when a reader sends out a signal and multiple RFID tags respond simultaneously. This is a problem with *cluster reading,* in which more than one tag is read at the same time. In such cases the tag identities cannot be read reliably. Some readers use an anti-collision system that is managed by a random number generator that issues orders on when readings are to be taken.[38] In addition, readers which are too closely spaced, and which have overlapping sensing fields, can interfere with one another and produce unintelligible data. The issues are being addressed with the development of new protocol standards which are likely to be based on the most common anti-collision methodologies: aloha and tree walking.[39] The aloha method assigns a time to each tag during which it is to communicate with the reader. The tree walking method instructs the tags to respond in the sequence that matches their serial numbers.

The higher the power level, the greater the distance from which the tag can be read. The power level is governed by laws which vary from country to country.[40] In the United States, the maximum permissible power at a frequency of 2.45 GHz, is approximately one hundred times the rate permitted in Europe. This equates to a difference in reading range of about one meter in the U.S. compared to one centimeter in Europe.

In general, the cost of the reader, and all of the components in the system, increases with the frequency of the signal. Although the price of the chip does not change based on frequency, the size of the antenna does and will therefore affect the size of the enclosure and thus the overall price of the tag.

The range of bandwidths that are associated with radio frequency extend from the Very Low Frequency (VLF) range of 10–30 kHz, to the Extremely High Frequency (EHF) range of 30–300 GHz.[41] Frequencies not only impact the distance between tag and reader but also affect the moving speed at which either can be sensed. In addition, the higher the frequency, the higher the rate of data transfer.

Frequencies reserved for RFID tend to be categorized into four groups, although there are eight ranges of frequencies used worldwide (each identified only by number), without standardization. One of the impediments to global implementation of RFID technology is the lack of standards and the failure of countries to agree on the allocation of their radio frequency spectrum. The frequencies generally applied for RFID are:

- *Low Frequency (LF)* RFID devices range from 124–125 kHz. At 125 kHz the operating range is up to one meter. This is the first frequency to be used in high volumes for commercial implementations including car immobilization and industrial applications. Tags using this frequency use wound coils, similar to those used in transformers, which can be made in a wide variety of shapes depending upon their intended use. The tag antenna serves as one winding of a transformer, and the scanner antenna serves as the other winding. This frequency has been used effectively for Electronic Article Surveillance (EAS) tags (see page 27).

- *High Frequency (HF)* is 13.56 MHz. This frequency is used primarily in the supply chain industry and has been applied to more than 100 million products. The frequency can be used without limitation worldwide, and has a range of approximately 1 meter in Europe and 0.8 meters (2.6') in the U.S. (given FCC and ECC power transmission limitations at these frequencies). Tag antennas manufactured at this frequency require just five to eight turns and are therefore relatively inexpensive. This frequency is used primarily for access control.

- *Ultra-High Frequency (UHF)* is 868–928 MHz. Tags manufactured at this frequency are generally made for macro-level applications, such as the tagging of large trans-ocean containers. The effective reading distance varies by country, with a distance of 2–3 meters in the U.S., and 0.7 meters (2.3') in Europe. The frequency can be used for both passive and active tagging systems. This frequency can not be used at all in Japan.[42]

- *Microwave* is 2.45 GHz. This frequency supports both active and passive tagging systems. Passive systems have a range of 30–50 cm (20") while active systems are used for long range.

In July 2003 Toppan Printing announced that it would start large-scale production of a dual-frequency RFID chip, named T-Junction, that will operate at 2.45 GHz, which is the common frequency used in Japan, and at 800–950 MHz, the band that is common in Europe and the United States. The chip, which will sell for about fifty cents, will consist of the chip and antenna mounted on a substrate, in other words, a finished label. In addition to the dual-frequency feature, Toppan will be selling reader modules that cost less than twenty dollars.[43]

RFID Tag Communication

RFID tags and readers communicate wirelessly through an air interface using a process called *coupling*. There are two types of coupling: inductive and propagation. Inductively coupled RFID tags (see Figure 6), that is, those that operate at a frequency of 125 kHz and 13.56 MHz, work similarly to a transformer, in that energy is transferred between two coils, one in the reader, the primary winding, and one in the tag antenna, the secondary winding. The number of turns in the coil and the size of the coil has a direct bearing on the range, with more turns and a larger size equating to a greater distance. The accuracy of the tag reading is also dependent on the power output by the reader, the tag's efficient power-conversion of that energy, the antenna's tuning, and the microcontroller's speed and data rate.[44] Propagating elec-

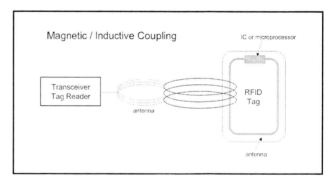

Figure 6. The inductive coupling communication process, which accounts for approximately 90% of all systems. (Illustration courtesy of Travis Sparks, University of North Carolina.)

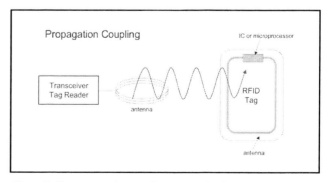

Figure 7. The propagation coupling communication process. (Illustration courtesy of Travis Sparks, University of North Carolina.)

tromagnetic waves, or *propagation coupling* (see Figure 7), enables reading over a longer distance.

Data travels through the air in the form of a carrier wave, or rhythmically varying sinusoidal field. The wave can be defined on the basis of three criteria: amplitude, frequency, and phase. The values of these criteria, which influence the modulation of the signal, have been defined in a number of standards. Regardless of the modulation, when data travels through the air it is susceptible to interference, such as other radio signals in the environment and other forms of noise which may produce distortion and error.

The RFID antenna is usually made of copper or aluminum due to their resistivity; however, if the read range is short, such as up to 10 cm, the antennas can be printed using conductive inks. There are many advantages to using printed antennas, such as, they:

- are less expensive
- can be printed using conventional printing presses
- can be manufactured at high speed
- can be printed on paper.

RFID and Paper Manufacturers

Work is underway to embed RFID tags into cartons during their fabrication, rather than to add them to the outside later, which not only could be more expensive but also would expose them to possible damage, sabotage, or vandalism. According to Sanjay Sarma, director of the MIT Auto-ID Center, the optimal RFID tag design "requires the careful coordination of IC design, antenna design, manufacturing process engineering, and paper engineering.[45] Westvaco, the second largest supplier of cartons and packaging,

has entered into a partnership with Checkpoint Systems Inc. to develop a system for embedding chips directly into cartons, although as of the fall of 2003 it is not believed that any have been shipped.[46]

The inclusion of RF security labels as source tagging for Electronic Article Surveillance (EAS) is not new. It is routinely done by incorporating an RF label either as part of the product itself or integrated in its packaging. The tags are often embedded between layers of paper, cardboard, or plastic blister packs. These labels do not have the capabilities that define RFID and are merely used for the protection of retail goods against theft.

RFID Smart Cards (Contactless Smart Cards)

RFID tags which are encased in credit-card-sized enclosures are used primarily for applications that require secure access, purchase payments, or data storage. The issue of range is not significant since the cards are normally used in proximity to the reader. Advantages of RFID Smart Cards, compared to other smart card technologies, are that card orientation is not significant, they are more reliable, and they work even when wet.

One of the most visible and popular examples of an RFID smart card is the Mobil and Exxon Speedpass, a

Figure 9. (A) The Gillette prototype smart shelf, at the MIT Auto-ID Center, looks like an ordinary store display. (B) The antenna, shown in full view in this prototype, senses the presence of merchandise containing RFID tags. In the production model the antenna will be hidden on the underside of a shelf. (C) The reader sitting atop the Savant computer will be affixed to the back of the shelf in the production model. (D) The contents of the smart shelf will be viewable by store management, or through the Internet, by people in the company headquarters (and elsewhere on an as-needed basis). (Photos by author.)

Figure 8. A sampling of Alien Technology chips scattered atop the surface of a dime. (Image ©2003, Alien Technology Corporation. Used with permission.)

In a fit of labor-saving gadget indulgence, I got myself a Speedpass the other day. You won't believe how convenient it is!

I was pumping gas at a station in Bushnell's Basin when I saw the brochure and was smitten with yearning.

"Got to have one of those," I muttered. So I went inside and told the cashier. She dialed a toll-free number and handed me her cordless phone.

A nice lady on the other end somewhere out of town answered and grilled me for 10 minutes about my identity and credit card billing matters.

Then she pronounced me a Speedpass owner and said it would soon arrive in the mail.

It came the other day. It's an ingenious little electronic device that attaches to the ring of your car keys along with the supermarket bonus card swipers.

(I've got all the good stuff.)

Here's what my smart little Speedpass does:

When I pull up for gas, I get out and casually pass my Speedpass over a symbol on the pump marked "Speedpass." (How about THAT!)

Almost instantly, the pump comes to life and the display tells me to remove the nozzle and select my octane grade and, finally "begin fueling."

That's all there is to it!

When I'm done I replace the nozzle and drive off.

When I got home after my maiden Speedpass experience, I could hardly wait to share my excitement with my wife.

"I've got this great thingy!" I said. "You won't believe it! I got one for you too!"

I told her how it works and said I'd take her out for her initiation and trial run next time she needed a fillup.

"Let me get this straight," she said. "You mean this little thing spares me the gross inconvenience of squandering the second it takes to swipe my credit card through the little slot?"

"Exactly," I said. "Is that great or what?"

"Gee, thanks, but wouldn't that mean I'd have to take my keys out of the ignition first?"

"Well...yeah, sure."

"I couldn't stand that inconvenience. Here's your extra thingy back. Forget it."

Isn't it weird how some women get no thrill out of technology for technology's sake?

I put her thingy on the dog's collar. He likes the tinkle it makes as it strikes against his license and rabies tag.

small fob which encloses a 134 kHz TI chip (see sidebar: "Listen to the Technology Freak Rhapsodize about His Speedpass"). The chip stores a serial number which is linked to the user's credit or debit card account. The system, which is also used in 430 McDonald's restaurants (FreedomPay) in Chicago and elsewhere, simplifies the payment process.

Alien Technology

In January 2003 Alien Technology[47] received a monumental order from The Gillette Company for one-half billion low-cost RFID tags, each about 350 μm, or approximately the size of a spec of dust (see Figure 8). The tags represent the first commercial implementation of the Auto-ID Center Electronic Product Code and will be used initially for tagging Gillette's two most pilfered products: Gillette Mach3 razor blades and Duracell multi-pack alkaline batteries. Gillette and its retailers lose tens of millions of dollars per year on the shrinkage[48] of these products. In many stores the items are kept in a locked case for security.

The Gillette order will enable a multi-year test of the EPC-enabled RFID tags through the Gillette supply chain. Gillette has also worked with the Auto-ID Center to develop smart shelving that incorporates a self-contained reader that senses the items that are on the shelf and notifies the stocking clerk when it needs to be replenished (Figure 9). The smart shelf can also be programmed to detect unusual buyer behaviors, such as removing four or more packages of razor blades, which might indicate a theft. In such a situation the reader would trigger a digital camera that would photograph the alleged thief, with the purloined goods in hand, and send the photo to store security.

The process of Fluidic Self Assembly (FSA), which is at the heart of Alien Technology's operations, was first proposed by researchers at the University of Berkeley in 1995. Alien is the first, and as yet the only, company to apply the technology for the mass production of nano devices through roll-to-roll manufacturing. The IC chips that Alien produces are approximately the size of a grain of sand and are barely perceptible to

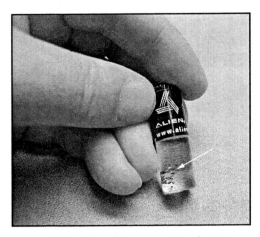

Figure 10. A vial containing approximately 150 NanoBlock ICs suspended in water. Each IC is 350 μm square. (Photo by author.)

Figure 11. Alien's first Fluidic Self Assembly manufacturing line in their Morgan Hill, CA facility. (Image ©2003, Alien Technology Corporation. Used with permission.)

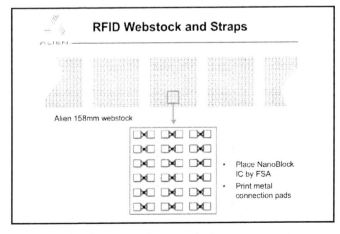

Figure 12. The Alien RFID IC chip is attached to an antenna using an adhesive strap. (Image ©2003, Alien Technology Corporation. Used with permission.)

the human eye (Figure 10). The actual sizes range form 10 μm to several hundred microns. The chips, which may be "as simple as a single transistor, or as complex as integrated circuits."[49] are fabricated on 12-in. crystal silicon wafers,[50] and the yields are therefore great, typically in the millions. The chip components can be tested while they are still a part of the wafer or can be tested wirelessly after they have been converted into finished RFID tags.

After separating the chips from the wafer through micromachining, they are etched, which produces a trapezoidal shape which Alien calls a Nanoblock™.[51] Complementary trapezoidal holes, or "receptors," are cut, etched, or laser drilled into the support substrate, and the chips, suspended in either water or alcohol, are poured over it. The chips flow into the holes in the substrate, which is moving as a web of plastic or as sheets of rigid material, through the fluidic self-assembly equipment (Figure 11). Millions of Nanoblocks can be placed in a matter of minutes, thousands in seconds. Any Nanoblocks that did not self-assemble are recycled. The Nanoblocks that did successfully seat into the holes are electrically connected to metallized support circuit patterns.

According to Dr. Paul Drzaic, vice president, Advanced Development Programs at Alien Technology, "We first manufacture straps (RFID IC plus two contact pads) that are connected to an antenna to form an inlet (Figure 12). The tag may have adhesive, graphical elements, etc., for attachment to or incorporation in an object (Figure 13)."[52]

The fluidic self-assembly process (Figure 14) can be used for purposes other than the manufacture of RFID tags. Active matrix electronic backplanes, composed on either a rigid (glass or plastic) or flexible (polyester, polyimide, polycarbonate, etc) substrate can be produced economically. Such backplanes can be used to control virtually all forms of current display technologies, including cholesteric, electroluminescent, electrophoretic, ferroelectric, field-emission, LCD, PDLC (Polymer Dispersed Liquid Crystal), and up- and/or down-converting phosphor displays (Figure 15). The FSA process supports the production of devices that are flexible and can conform to various shapes and contours. In addition, size is a major advantage. According to an Alien Technology White Paper, FSA has "genuine potential for making very large, light weight, low power, wall hung televisions."[53]

Dr. Drzaic reports that the company is producing a Class 1 tag (Figure 16) selling for about a nickel in volumes of billions, and that their battery-assisted tags are on a "rapid cost reduction pathway, reaching a few dollars each in three years."[54] The nickel tags will be used for both supply chain (logistics) and authentication (anti-counterfeit) applications. They anticipate a capacity of

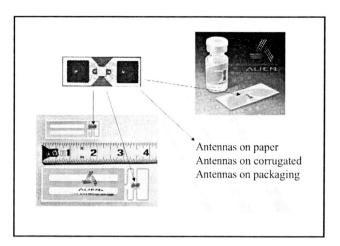

Figure 13. Straps are the carriers by which the Alien RFID ICs are adhered to a variety of antenna designs matched to particular applications. (Image ©2003, Alien Technology Corporation. Used with permission.)

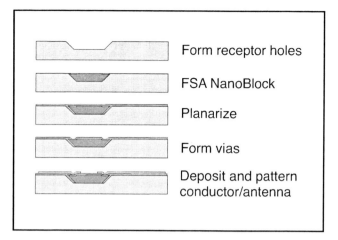

Form receptor holes

FSA NanoBlock

Planarize

Form vias

Deposit and pattern conductor/antenna

Figure 14. A cross-section view of the fluidic self-assembly process. (Image ©2003, Alien Technology Corporation. Used with permission.)

one billion straps per year by 2005 and ten billion by 2006. Despite the likelihood that Alien will be able to sell whatever it can produce, Dr. Drzaic predicts that RFID tags and UPC bar codes are likely not only to coexist during the transition period but also to be fabricated as a single unit.

The Hitachi µ-Chip (mu-chip)

The smallest RFID chip yet developed is the Hitachi µ-Chip (Figure 17), which measures 0.3 mm square with features that are 0.18 µm. The chip, introduced in February 2003 in prototype form, can store a 128-bit number (128-bit ROM) which is written on the chip during manufacture and can not be changed. The numbering system, developed by Hitachi, is based on the "mu-chip ID number criterion." µ-Chips operate at 2.45 GHz and can be read from about one foot away (30 cm).

In addition to its unique size, the chip incorporates a novel means of attaching an antenna. The chip's electrodes, one at the top and one on the bottom, make it easier to fabricate the chip into a finished RFID tag. A more advanced version of the chip, introduced in September 2003, has been developed with an antenna on the micro-integrated circuit chip. The antenna is produced using bump-metallization technology, which is used in conventional chip fabrication. This µ-Chip is capable of transmitting data contact-free. Hitachi expects to sell a complete system consisting of tags, readers, soft-

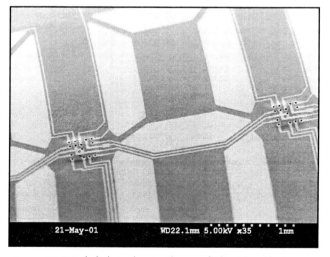

Figure 15. Detailed photo showing the use of Alien Nanoblocks controlling seven-segment display components. (Image ©2001, Alien Technology Corporation. Used with permission.)

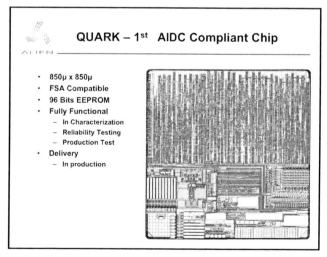

QUARK – 1st AIDC Compliant Chip

- 850µ x 850µ
- FSA Compatible
- 96 Bits EEPROM
- Fully Functional
  - In Characterization
  - Reliability Testing
  - Production Test
- Delivery
  - In production

Figure 16. An enlargement of the surface real estate residing on the first Auto-ID compliant chip. (Image ©2003, Alien Technology Corporation. Used with permission.)

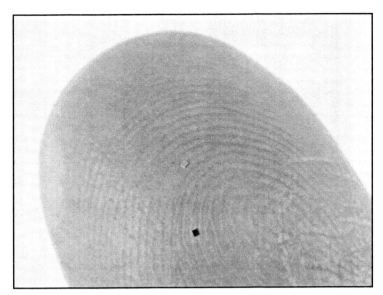

Figure 17. The minute Hitachi µ-Chip is small enough to embed in virtually any product without detection or visible alteration. (Photo courtesy of Hitachi.)

broken. The sensor, which is enzyme-based, responds to temperature over a span of time that approximates the duration of the supply chain (Figure 19). If the temperature reaches an unacceptable level it breaks the electrical circuit. The breaks in the circuit can be read with a hand-held scanner (Figure 20), and the time of each temperature change can be determined. The scan can provide accurate details as to when (and therefore, where) the spoilage occurred, and the chill chain can be "repaired" to avoid further problems.

The use of the biosensor system enables the retailer to apply a "Best If Used By" date to the product based upon the history of its actual storage life, rather than relying on an "Expiration" date that had been estimated when the product was produced in the factory. The actual remaining shelf life can be determined when the product is received at the retail location.

Product Integrity: Counterfeiting

The proliferation of fake products has reached crisis proportions in many parts of the world. Of particular concern is the counterfeiting of pharmaceuticals in the form of inferior and potentially fatal drugs. Such products not only fail to cure the disease for which they are taken, but they endanger the health, and even the life, of the person taking them. Worldwide, the amount of pharmaceutical counterfeiting is estimated at 2%, although it is as high as 12% in Russia and 80% in Peru.[56] RFID tagging technology can be applied to drug packaging to ensure an unbroken chain of possession and to interrogate sealed containers and blister packs without opening them.

ware, and networking infrastructure in 2005. Among its expected applications is for use in paper-based items having a commercially recognized face value, such as gift certificates, bonds, or currency.

Enhanced RFID Tags

RFID tags are highly effective communication devices that can, depending on their type, both send and receive data. The data that they transmit may have been permanently manufactured into the tag logic, may have been acquired by the tag at one or more points after manufacture, or may have been recorded from a sensor that has been constructed as part of a specialty tag design. Sensors may use any of a number of technologies, including acoustic, chemical, magnetic, photonic, pressure, thermo, or radiation.

The need for close scrutiny over the movement of goods to market applies most particularly to food and pharmaceuticals, which are susceptible to spoilage. If undetected, sold, and consumed it can lead to dire consequences such as illness or death. The U.S. Food and Drug Administration estimates that as much as 20% of food produced in the United States is thrown away due to spoilage.[55] One of the first examples of a special-purpose food monitoring tag (Figure 18) is the Bioett Time Temperature Indicator (TTI), which consists of a chipless RFID and MicroElectricalMechanical Systems (MEMS) biosensor.

The self-adhesive biosensor, which is about the size of a credit card, is used to ensure that the chill chain between food processor and food retailer has not been

Figure 18. The Bioett biosensor includes a UPC code on its surface so that it can be scanned using conventional retail readers. (Photo courtesy of Bioett.)

Figure 19. The Bioett Aktivator is located at the food packing site and produces the temperature-sensitive labels just prior to their application. (Photo courtesy of Bioett.)

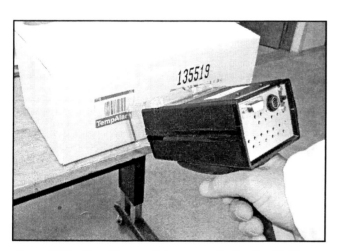

Figure 20. The Bioett biosensor is interrogated with a hand-held scanner which detects any lapses in the chill chain. (Photo courtesy of Bioett.)

Another problem related to drugs is the illegal resale of government-subsidized medical aid, particularly in the form of AIDS drugs. Heavily discounted AIDS medications are sent to countries in Africa, for example, diverted through criminally supported gray markets, and resold in their country of origin. The use of RFID tagging would make it possible to track the source of the drugs and stop the illegal trafficking.

Smart Packaging

Smart packaging, or *intelligent packaging*, is defined as any package that incorporates a form of radio tagging that enables it to be sensed from a distance or is printed with inks or labeled with sensors that can respond to environmental changes and react accordingly. This change may be exhibited by a transformation in ink color or the display of a warning symbol or text on a sensor. The intelligence that is added to the package provides responsive technologies that may communicate additional product tracking information to those who handle it along the supply chain or to the end-user who determines its freshness or other salient quality. The market for intelligent packaging is predicted by Pira International to double between the period of 2002 and 2007.[57] The application of polymer electronics, in the form of printed components, are likely to become part of a package itself.

A variation of smart packaging is *active packaging*. According to Robert Shimmin, writing in *Labels & Labelling* magazine, active packaging "is designed to change the condition of the contents [of the package] in order to extend shelf-life or improve product safety."[58] Active packaging may incorporate any of the following technologies:

- **Moisture Absorbers.** Packages may incorporate absorbers or desiccants that can soak up excessive moisture. The package label or the wrapping material may incorporate such materials.

- **Gas Indicators.** A printed layer or laminated polymer film may serve as a color change indicator to show the presence of oxygen, which impacts on the "perishability" of certain foods.

- **Active Films.** This developing category of packaging uses nanotechnology to produce materials that can respond to their environment, sensing light or heat or changes in gas or pH.

- **Light-Activated Valves.** A "valve" layer can be applied over a porous layer so that the pores will be exposed under a set of engineered circumstances.

- **Pump Action.** Gel materials that substantially change volume in response to a stimulus can be designed into packages to produce a pumping action that might be used to remove excessive gas from a package or initiate some other valuable action.

- **Light Reaction.** The diffraction of light off of inexpensive dielectric mirrors that have been made from the self-assembly of block copolymers can be applied for decorative or security packaging features.

- **Time Temperature Indicators/Freshness Indicators.** See Enhanced RFID Tags: Bioett Time Temperature Indicator, page 20

- **Heat-Sensitive Inks.** Thermochromic inks, which react to changes in temperature, will either disappear or change color when the ambient temperature around them exceeds their set level. Some inks respond to ranges of cold temperatures and have been used for wine labels to indicate, through the display of a certain color, when a bottle is properly chilled.

- **Light-Sensitive Inks.** Photochromic inks react to changes in light (either ultraviolet or natural light) by changing color. They may be applied to packaging to verify its authenticity or used for specialty advertising applications.[59]

Smart Documents

Various forms of paper used in business transactions, instruments of commerce, correspondence, and information archiving can be intelligence enabled through the use of RFID tags. The process of embedding ultra-thin RFID tags in valuable and potentially valuable paper materials, such as money, passports, visas, stock certificates, bonds, and other forms of commercial paper, can provide many benefits, including:

- Ensuring that the paper is authentic and is "as represented" in its printed appearance.

- Verifying that the value printed on the face of the document is its true and unadulterated value.

- Storing confidential information that should be hidden from those who routinely handle the document.

- Storing a record of the chain of custody to verify its history of ownership.

According to Bruce James, Public Printer of the United States, "There are already things in the passport you have that you cannot see that help prevent counterfeiting. We are developing sets of skills that make it nearly impossible to counterfeit. You can look to see microchips in the next generation of passports, so when you present it to a customs agent, they scan the chip and it presents an image of you on their screen to authenticate who you are. We are looking at a lot of things like this."[60] In the summer of 2003, three French companies jointly developed Intelligent Film for Identification (IFI), which uses RFID to store all of the data contained in the printed passport as well as biometric data, such as a fingerprint or iris scan.[61]

Smart RFID Labels

Philips[62] I-CODE is an RFID tagging product that has been deployed successfully in many environments. It has been marketed, for example, as a turnkey solution to libraries as a comprehensive inventory management system. A smart label containing an I-CODE chip is affixed to every item, including books, records, maps, videotapes, discs, artwork, and other forms of media that a library lends. Each of the chips contains 512-bit read/write memory and has a unique serial number which is then assigned to the object that it protects. Readers can be installed in all of the stacks so that the location of every item can be determined instantly, even if it is misfiled.

Library patrons are issued plastic cards that also contain the I-CODE chip. As library patrons pass through a gate with the items that they intend to borrow, the objects are automatically recognized and assigned to their accounts. The I-CODE system has a built-in anti-collision capability so that multiple items can be read accurately.

Items that are returned to the library can be checked in automatically by placing them in a drop box which has a reader in the flap of its door.

The I-CODE 1 smart label ICs enable the production of labels as small as 2×2 cm and a thickness of less than 0.5 mm. They are small enough to be manufactured in laminated form between layers of paper or plastic. Philips has also used the technology for disposable smart bag tags used for airline baggage handling. The I-CODE chip, with an antenna, is sandwiched between two layers of paper and can be read at distances of up to 1.2 meters.

Animal Tracking and Control

The world's human population is approximately six billion people,[63] with a population of livestock animals of more than four billion.[64] Most countries conduct a census to learn about the numbers and characteristics of its population; however, the collection of data concerning livestock is often haphazard or nonexistent. This is a significant problem since animals provide much of the human food supply. It is standard operating procedure for national fast food restaurant chains and food retailers to require detailed records concerning the health history of animals before buying their meat and serving it to the public. It is therefore vital that processes and procedures are in place to ensure food safety, to manage the pre-market feeding and care of animals, to monitor and control their health, and to prevent their loss due to theft or straying.

RFID technology provides some excellent solutions to these problems in the form of tags that can be applied to animals either externally or internally. Passive RFID tags can be used for identification and can be utilized in a data-gathering system to record animal history such as injections, growth rate, milk production, etc. Data is collected by using either a hand scanner or walking the animal through a tunnel scanner. Injectable RFID microchip technology, such as Digital Angel's BioThermo,[65] can be implanted under an animal's skin to monitor its health, storing its temperature and movement data. Eventually the chip will incorporate GPS technology so that the animal's location, either on the farm or in the supply chain, can be monitored.

The RFID Push from the Market

The world's largest and most complex commercial database contains more than 200 terabytes and is used to manage one of the most sophisticated retail operations anywhere: Wal-Mart. The database is second in size only to that of the Pentagon. Wal-Mart, the world's largest retailer, sells more than 120,000 different items, and is unique in many respects, one of which is their policy of sharing database information with their suppliers in a process they call "Collaborative Planning, Forecasting and Replenishment." On a daily basis they send their suppliers reports of how much of their products they have sold, and how much they expect to sell.

Wal-Mart's sales predictions are based on multi-year analyses of sales and include several factors, such as weather and holidays and their effect on individual stores. Weather forecasts, for example, are entered into the system daily and will affect the shipment of fewer or more snow shovels in January or fewer or more cases of soda in July. Wal-Mart's buying power enables them to place significant pressure on their suppliers to provide goods when they need them and in the specified form and amount. For certain high-theft items, Wal-Mart requires that suppliers insert Electronic Article Surveillance (EAS) tags at the manufacturing source and at no additional cost to Wal-Mart. While the EAS tags are only of benefit to the retailer, the use of RFID tags would provide benefits to all points along the supply chain.[66]

Wal-Mart (which owns Sam's Club) and many of its major suppliers are members of the Auto-ID Center,[67] and have made commitments to implementing RFID technology. Wal-Mart began its testing with pallets of Proctor & Gamble paper towels that were RFID-tagged and delivered to a Sam's Club in Tulsa, Oklahoma. That test was followed by one that included tagged pallets from multiple vendors delivered to both a Wal-Mart and Sam's Club in Tulsa.[68] On the basis of those tests, Wal-Mart CIO Linda Dillman announced on June 11, 2003, at the Retail Systems 2003/VICS Collaborative Commerce Conference that they were requesting their one hundred largest suppliers to affix RFID tags using the EPC on pallets and cases by January 1, 2005.[69] On an annual basis the company receives approximately one billion cases from its top one hundred suppliers, and expects, on a gradual basis, that they will comply. Dillman said that she expects that the company would eventually issue a compliance order to its suppliers. "It will become a requirement, like EDI, because if we can't track your product with [EPC tags], it's an added cost for us that we have to pass on to our customers."[70]

In addition to the efficiencies that are inherent in using RFID, Wal-Mart stands to benefit significantly on its bottom line. AMR Research analyst Peter Abell estimates that 10% of Wal-Mart's overall sales costs are related to the supply chain, that is, storing, transporting, and taking inventory of goods. That amount could be reduced by 3–4% which, based on revenues in 2002, could save $1.3 to $1.5 billion.[71] Their suppliers are likely to benefit as well. Proctor & Gamble predicts that the efficiencies gained from the use of RFID tags will result in a potential inventory reduction of 40%, or $1.5 billion, which could allow them to reduce costs by up to 4 cents per dollar in every transaction.[72]

It is unknown how suppliers will implement the tagging. It is speculated that corrugated packaging manufacturers may be asked to manufacture the tags directly in the cartons. However it is done, Wal-Mart's initial plan will require about one billion tags, which is an especially significant number given that established tag manufacturers do not have the capacity to provide them. Texas Instruments, Inc., for example, had only shipped 200 million tags as of the summer of 2003, and most of those tags were in the price range of 30 to 50 cents each. Wal-Mart's target tag price is 5 cents.[73] Although Wal-Mart's commitment to RFID is significant, Kevin Ashton, executive director of the MIT Auto-ID Center, says that widespread adoption could take until 2010 or longer.[74]

Although Wal-Mart's initial implementation will be at the carton-level, they are also experimenting with smart shelving which can automatically sense the presence of RFID-tagged items. The shelf-level sensing helps the store management detect theft and also maintain adequate stocking. Out-of-stock situations often result in lost sales, and stock that sits in the back room is not producing revenue.[75]

RFID Field Trials

The first field trial of the system developed by the Auto-ID Center was implemented in Tulsa, OK, in the form of a simple supply chain test that tracked the movement of a single SKU from factory to retail store. The tagging was applied only to the pallets, which originated at one factory and bypassed distribution centers, being sent instead directly to the retail outlet. The elements of the test were these:

- The manufacturer was the Proctor & Gamble factory in Cape Giradeau, MO. They used wooden pallets manufactured by Chep with preinstalled 915 MHz RFID tags. Two tags were installed at opposite corners of the pallet to ensure reliable scanning. Portal readers from Savi were installed at both the factory and retailer to interrogate the pallets.

- The product was Bounty paper towels which is one of the highest volume products sold at the retailer. The fact that the item would need to be restocked often, and would generate high rates of data for the study, was one of the reasons for its selection.

- The retailer was Sam's Club in Tulsa, OK.

The historic "beep heard around the world," as described by Kevin Ashton, founder and executive director of the MIT Auto-ID Center, occurred on Monday, October 1, 2001, when the first shipment of Bounty pallets left the factory in Missouri. It represented the first reading of an EPC. The next day the shipment arrived at Sam's Club, and the second EPC was recorded. Empty pallets were recorded from October 4–30 as they exited the Sam's Club loading dock. As that was happening, Center sponsors were able to access the data via the Internet, showing the geographic location of the scan, the reader ID, the EPC number, the product, its manufacturer, and the time and date.

The result of the test was that 78% of all of the tags that passed through a portal reader were read. Since each pallet had two tags, the effective reading success rate was 97%. Misreads that occurred were attributed both to hardware and human failures and included such things as power outages, frequency interference, improperly stacked pallets, inoperative tags, and a failed hard drive. Some of the human errors included turning off the system, using pallets without tags, or passing through a portal that did not have a reader.[76]

RFID and Privacy

Concerns over the potential for invasion of privacy through the use of RFID are of real concern. The planting of a "bug" to track an individual is no longer a spy movie fantasy. Although the implications of providing communication capabilities in virtually all consumer goods are unknown, they are fraught with the opportunity for sinister activities.

A group named CASPIAN (Consumers Against Supermarket Privacy Invasion and Numbering) has been formed to challenge attempts by retailers to capture and track consumer transactions and behaviors. CASPIAN has drafted the RFID Right to Know Act of 2003, which is proposed legislation dealing with how RFID-enabled products are to be labeled and what consumer privacy protections should be in place (see sidebar: RFID Right to Know Act of 2003). They and other consumer advocates see a major threat to privacy in a future world in which every item has a unique ID. The identification contained in a tag, which is a size somewhere between a grain of sand and speck of dust, can be hidden within an object or its packaging, out of sight of the consumer.

Figure 21. CASPIAN, an organization of consumer advocates launched a successful campaign against Benetton's intended use of RFID tagging of its clothing.
http://www.boycottbenetton.org/PR_030313a.html

Consumers are likely to be unaware of their presence or the personal information that may be gathered regarding their buying habits or other behaviors.

Katherine Albrecht, the founder and director of CASPIAN, fears the future portrayed in videos produced by Proctor and Gamble, in which consumers might expect "shopping carts that automatically bill consumer's account (cards would no longer be needed to link purchases to individuals), refrigerators that report their contents to the supermarket for re-ordering, and interactive televisions that select commercials based on the contents of a home's refrigerator."[77] Albrecht has said of RFID: "Ultimately, this technology will enslave humanity."[78]

An early battle in the concern over consumer privacy and the potential impact of RFID was won by CASPIAN, which launched a boycott against Benetton (Figure 21), an Italian clothing manufacturer that had supposedly announced its plans on March 11, 2003, to embed RFID chips in 15 million of its clothing items. Benetton stated on April 4, 2003, that it would not move forward with its planned use of RFID, although it did not state that it would never implement item-level tagging.

The action by CASPIAN was apparently caused by confusion produced by the press release issued by Philips on March 11, which contained erroneous information. According to a report in the *RFID Journal*, the confusion occurred because the person doing the RFID testing at Lab ID (http://www.lab-id.com/) is named Mauro Benetton. According to Mr. Benetton, "...the fact that my name is Benetton made Philips think that the technology was being used by Benetton, but it wasn't."[79]

CASPIAN's position, as stated by Katherine Albrecht, was that "Benetton could easily link your name and credit card information to the serial number in your sweater, in essence 'registering' that sweater to you. Then any time you go near an RFID reader device, the sweater could beam out your identity to anyone with access to the database—all without your knowledge or permission."[80]

To allay fears of after-purchase surveillance, RFID tags may incorporate a "kill" fea-

---

RFID Right to Know Act of 2003: Summary

Proposed legislation to mandate labeling of RFID-enabled products and consumer privacy protections

This is a summary of the RFID Right to Know Act of 2003 which can be found in its entirety at http://www.nocards.org/rfid/rfidbill.shtml. Reprinted with permission.

SUMMARY OF THE BILL
AN ACT
To require that commodities containing radio frequency identification tags bear labels stating that fact, to protect consumer privacy, and for other purposes.

SEC. 1. SHORT TITLE.
This section shortens the title of the bill to "RFID Right to Know Act of 2003."

SEC. 2. AMENDMENTS TO THE FAIR PACKAGING AND LABELING PROGRAM.
This section amends the Fair Packaging and Labeling Program by inserting language under subsection (a) of paragraph (6). This section requires that a consumer commodity or package that contains or bears a radio frequency identification tag shall bear a label as provided in the paragraph below.

It also defines the term "radio frequency identification" or "RFID" to mean technologies that use radio waves to automatically identify individual items. It defines the term "tag" to mean a microchip that is attached to an antenna and is able to transmit identification information.

Finally it describes that the label should state, at a minimum, that the consumer commodity or package contains or bears a radio frequency identification tag, and that the tag can transmit unique identification information to an independent reader both before and after purchase; and be in a conspicuous type-size and location and in print that contrasts with the background against which it appears.

SEC. 3. AMENDMENTS TO THE FEDERAL FOOD, DRUG, AND COSMETIC ACT RELATING TO MISBRANDING.
This section amends the federal Food, Drug and Cosmetic Act by inserting language under the sections relating to misbranding of commodities. It says that a food, cosmetic, drug or device is misbranded if the product or package contains an RFID tag, unless it bears a label stating, at a minimum, that the consumer commodity or package contains or bears a radio frequency identification tag, and that the tag can transmit unique identification information to an independent reader both before and after purchase. It also prescribes that the label must be in a conspicuous type-size and prominent location and in print that contrasts with the background against which it appears.

SEC. 4. AMENDMENTS TO THE FEDERAL ALCOHOL ADMINISTRATION ACT.

This section states that a person shall not manufacture, import, or bottle for sale or distribution in the United States any alcoholic beverage unless its container bears a label. That label must state at a minimum, that container contains or bears a radio frequency identification tag, and that the tag can transmit unique identification information to an independent reader both before and after purchase. The label must also be in a conspicuous type-size and prominent location and in print that contrasts with the background against which it appears.

SEC. 5. AMENDMENTS TO TITLE 15, CHAPTER 36—CIGARETTE LABELING AND ADVERTISING.

This section states that a person shall not manufacture, import, or package for sale or distribution in the United States any cigarettes unless its container bears a label. That label must state at a minimum, that container contains or bears a radio frequency identification tag, and that the tag can transmit unique identification information to an independent reader both before and after purchase. The label must also be in a conspicuous type-size and prominent location and in print that contrasts with the background against which it appears.

SEC. 6. AMENDMENTS TO TITLE 15, CH. 94—PRIVACY.

This section goes directly to protecting the privacy of consumers. First it directs that a business shall not combine or link an individual's nonpublic personal information with RFID tag identification information, beyond what is required to manage inventory. Second, a business shall not, directly or through an affiliate, disclose to a nonaffiliated third party an individual's nonpublic personal information in association with RFID tag identification information. Third, a business shall not, directly or through an affiliate or nonaffiliated third party, use RFID tag identification information to identify an individual.

Next, this section directs the Federal Trade Commission to establish appropriate standards for the businesses described in the previous paragraph. The safeguards should: insure the integrity and confidentiality of an individual's records and information; insure that RFID tag records do not identify individuals; protect against anticipated threats or hazards to the security of an individual's records and information; and protect an individual against substantial harm or inconvenience, which may result from unauthorized access to or use of an individual's records and information.

The third section covers consumer and business education. It directs the Federal Trade Commission to publish and disseminate documents with the purpose of educating the general public about RFID technology. The documents, at a minimum, shall describe RFID technology and how companies, marketers and government agencies can use RFID technology to collect an individual's nonpublic personal information.

It also directs the Federal Trade Commission to publish and disseminate documents with the purpose of educating businesses about RFID technology and the importance of protecting an individual's privacy. The documents, at a minimum, shall describe RFID technology, advocate privacy protection, and explain how businesses must conform their actions to comply with the provisions of this Act.

The last three sections relate to state laws, rulemaking and provides general definitions. The bill states that a State may afford an individual greater protection than the protection provided under this subchapter. It also states that the Federal Trade Commission shall prescribe regulations necessary to carry out and enforce the mandate of this subchapter. Finally the bill provides term definitions. The term "radio frequency identification" or "RFID" means technologies that use radio waves to automatically identify individual items. The term "tag" means a microchip that is attached to an antenna and can transmit identification information. The term "business" means a corporation, partnership or other entity that collects or aggregates an individual's nonpublic personal information. Finally, the term "nonpublic personal information" means information that a business can use to identify an individual. Such information includes, at a minimum, name, address, social security number, and financial data.

ture, wherein the chip can be deactivated at checkout, as suggested in the Auto-ID Center's technical specifications. It may be an unjustified fear since in most cases the tag will be incorporated in product packaging, not in the product itself, so that the tags will be disposed of by the consumer. In addition, the range of an RFID tag is very limited and would not likely be sensed by someone outside the home or from a remote location.

Nonetheless there is always the fear of *function creep*,[51] which is the condition that arises when a technology implemented for one purpose is applied to one that was unintended…sometimes with negative consequences. Be that as it may, people have the opportunity to "get chipped" and have an RFID tag implanted in their bodies so that their identities are beyond question (Figure 22).

There may be significant benefits in keeping tags alive beyond their supply chain life. There are likely many logical reasons to extend their usefulness, such as if:

- The consumer decides to return the item to the store and it must re-enter the store's inventory. In such a case the store benefits by being able to identify with certainty that the item did, in fact, come out of its inventory. It can use a reader at the return desk and easily reenter the item back into inventory. In addition, goods that are returned due to defects or performance problems can be identified by place, date, and time of manufacture and returned to the manufacturer, providing valuable product-specific information.

- Items are returned on the basis of a product recall. They can be identified easily, and their purchase price credited to the consumer's account.

- Tagged items can interact with RFID-enabled appliances in the home. A washing machine, for example, can automatically adjust to the fabric care instructions stored in the tags embedded in clothing, a microwave can self-adjust to properly cook foods with embedded tags in their packaging, and a refrigerator can sense the products that are stored on its

shelves and produce a shopping list based on expiration dates or other criteria.

- Smart homes can react to the use of objects and respond with useful services. A tag in a shaver, for example, might signal displays in a mirror to show the weather report, morning, news, and new email (Figure 23).

- Recycling facilities can read the tags to sort items automatically so that they can be remanufactured into new products.

Electronic Article Surveillance (EAS)

Electronic Article Surveillance (EAS) systems utilize RFID, as well as other technologies, for preventing theft and shoplifting. EAS RFID tags are usually small white oblong-shaped pieces of plastic that are attached to items as an anti-shoplifting strategy (Figure 24). The RFID tags

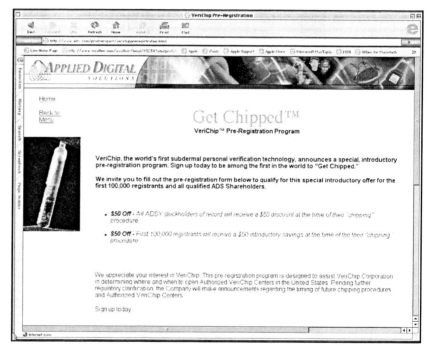

Figure 22. Applied Digital Solutions offers the VeriChip, a human-implantable RFID tag that ensures absolute identification. The nonvisible text on the above screen reads as follows: Consumer Disclosure: By submitting the pre-registration form, the customer has no obligation to purchase the product at any future date. VeriChip Corporation is not obligated to have, or place, an authorized VeriChip Center in the proximity of the registrant's address. Currently, the company is establishing new centers in various locations throughout the country—Please see the authorized VeriChip Centers web page for a location nearest you. Only one discount may be used per person. For more information, please call the VeriChip Call Center at 1-800-970-CHIP. (Applied Digital Solutions Incorporated, 400 Royal Palm Way, Suite 410, Palm Beach, Florida 33480, phone: 561/805-8000, fax: 561/805-8001, web: http://www.adsx.com.)

are usually disposable and are made to respond to a specific frequency that is emitted by the transmitter portion of the exit portal reader. The tag's response to the frequency is read by a receiver, which is located directly across from the transmitter. If the tag has not been deactivated, the frequency will be passed to the receiver, and an alarm will sound. The readers, which are familiar gates found in most retail stores, are placed at exit portals to detect the passage of any tags that have not been deactivated at the checkout counter (Figure 25). The gates themselves are a visible deterrent since the antenna loop could be installed invisibly around the exit door. Many large retailers require their suppliers to ship them goods with the EAS tags already embedded in the product packaging. This *source tagging*, which occurs either during manufacture or packaging, is a growing phenomenon.

Source tagging is of three types. The first is *topical source tagging* in which the tag is applied to the outside of the product and is likely visible. The second is *internal source tagging*, wherein the tag is placed inside the packaging, out of view of the consumer. The third option is *source integration*, whereby the tag is manufactured either within the product itself or embedded in the packaging material.[82]

All in all, close to one million EAS systems have been installed worldwide, mostly to protect consumer goods. The systems enable merchandisers to keep goods out on display rather than locked in cases or stored behind a counter out of view. The tags do not identify items on an individual basis—their attachment is solely to protect the item from removal from the premises if it has not been purchased. When the item is purchased, the tag is either removed, if it is reusable, or deactivated with a hand-held scanner or by passing it over a pad so that it does not activate the reader at the store exit and sound an alarm.

The EAS RFID tags are generally small, about 3 cm square (1.18-in.) and consist of a thin etched aluminum helical antenna that is affixed to a paper base. The tags, which are chipless, can be produced to look like a normal retail tag, with a bar code, price, and other typical product information. The antenna terminates with either an RC component or a diode, which serves the purpose of emitting a radio signal in response to the signal that the antenna has received. When the tag is disarmed it is exposed to an RF pulse that is several times stronger than that used to interrogate the tag, and the pulse burns out the electronic components on the tag so that it can pass through the exit reader without setting off its alarm. A new type of chipless

Figure 23. LCD monitors embedded in a bathroom mirror respond with user-specific information in response to an RFID tag contained in the shaver. This concept photo was taken in the Philips HomeLab research facility. (Photo courtesy of Royal Philips Electronics.)

Figure 24 (A). A standard EAS security tag. (B). An EAS tag that serves double duty by carrying the UPC bar code on its surface. (Photo by author.)

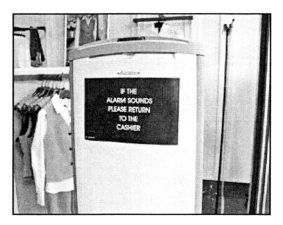

Figure 25. One section of an EAS security portal produced by Sensormatic. (Photo by author.)

tag called a SAW (Surface Acoustic Wave) device can be used for EAS applications and can be made with temperature-sensing capability.

The objective of EAS is to deter theft; however, some tag technologies go beyond that by providing a "benefit denial." Should an item with an EAS tag that is filled with specially formulated ink capsules be successfully stolen from a store, the item would be ruined if the thief attempted to break off the tag. Such tags, sometimes called "alligators," require a special tool for proper removal. IDTechEx Limited of Cambridge, UK, predicts that by the year 2010 the global RFID market will be composed of 70% chip and 30% chipless RFID tags.[83]

Identifying and Tagging Everything

Examples of RFID tagging technology that are in use (•) or that have been demonstrated in lab environments (-•-) include those that have been:

- Applied to airline luggage that has been identified at the ticket counter as belonging to a suspicious individual. The selected luggage is diverted through a scanner-sensor to an area for hand inspection.

- Applied to airline food carts to track their locations and to schedule repair and replacement. A system can be enabled that will activate the brakes on a cart if it is moved outside a prescribed zone.

- Attached to expensive assets to guard against unlawful removal and to maintain an accurate and timely inventory.

- Used for VIP Gold Card and FastTrack access to airport and other commercial parking lots.

- Embedded in plastic smart cards that are used for secured entry into gated communities, office buildings, private offices, laboratories, and other limited-access areas.

- Designed into a self-checkout library system in which those borrowing books can automatically check them out and in.

- Used to manage a fleet of airport vehicles as a security measure.

- Manufactured into tires so that they can be linked to the vehicle identification number (VIN) of the vehicle on which they are mounted. The read/write tags can store information about the date and place of manufacture, its maximum inflation pressure, size, etc. In addition, instrumentation can be built into the car's dashboard to display the tire pressure in each tire, including the spare.

- Integrated by many car manufacturers into car keys. The car will not start unless the reader inside the steering column senses the serial number of the car.

- Used in a temperature-sensing enhanced RFID tags to monitor the storage life of perishable goods, such as human blood.

- Attached to the inside windshields of cars to enable automatic payment of road tolls. The first electronic tolling system was placed into operation in 1991 in Oklahoma.

- Sandwiched between layers of plastic to form a debit card used for rapid payment in fast-food restaurants and for other commercial transactions.

- Applied to letters, parcels, and packages to track their movement through a postal system.

- Incorporated in employee badges to record arrival and departure times for attendance.

- Accepted by the world's three largest seaport operators as a security measure to protect the more than 17,000 containers which arrive in U.S. ports daily. Fewer than 2% of the containers are opened and inspected. Initially only a small percentage of

Figure 26. RFID tags are a significant component of the Hasbro Star Wars CommTech™ (Communication Output Memory Module-powered) toy system. The CommTech chips, which are provided for each Star Wars action figure, contain RFID tags (see inset in the upper right corner showing an enlargement of the antenna lines and the IC chip) that enable the figures to speak using the CommTech Reader (pictured in the bottom half of the photo). Thirty-five million tags were produced, at a cost of about ten cents each. The readers retailed for about twenty dollars each. This toy line, introduced in 2000, was the first to use RFID technology. The only other toy to utilize RFID, as of this writing, is the Microsoft Barney, which achieves interactivity through RFID. (Photo by author.)

containers will be tracked. It is part of the Department of Transportation's "Smart and Secure Tradelanes" (SST) program.

- Added to the casing of printer ink cartridges to guarantee that only bona fide replacements are installed in the printer.

- Attached to rental cars to positively identify abandoned or misplaced vehicles.

- Affixed to runner's shoes to sense the start and stop time in marathons and other competitive events.

- Attached or implanted into farm animals to control their feeding, record their vital statistics, and maintain health records.

- Secured to precision tooling equipment to track hours of usage and removal from operation when necessary.

- Attached to bins, totes, containers, tubs, and pallets to move them appropriately along an automated production line.

- Mounted on the nose of race cars to monitor their progress on the track and their location at the finish line.

- Used in toys, such as Hasbro's Star Wars CommTech, to activate a voice or other action based on proximity (Figure 26).

- Embedded into high-end fashion merchandise to validate its authenticity as it moves through the supply chain.

- Incorporated into the infrastructure of the sales floor of the Prada Epicenter in New York City (Figure 27). When clothing, which contains RFID tags, is taken to the fitting room and hung up, information about the item appears on a large LCD screen.

- Adhered to test tubes and lab samples so that the content can be identified by sample number, date, and time. The tag is not affected by extremes in temperature.

- Attached to containers deployed to armed forces troops stationed around the world, including supplies shipped for Operation Desert Storm. According to Maj. Forrest Burke, chief of logis-

Figure 27. The Prada Epicenter store in Soho in New York City is so exclusive that it does not have a name on the exterior. The store, which is said to have cost $40 million, has clearly visible Texas Instruments RFID tags on most of its merchandise. Information about any article can be determined by using a hand-held scanner or carrying the item into a changing room. Photography was not allowed inside the store. (Photo by the author.)

tics information management at the Coalition Forces Land Component Command, "This is an information-centric war and logistics is at the heart of it."[84]

- Applied to drug labels for sight-impaired people so that when the bottle is brought in proximity to the reader, the person can hear the prescription instructions.

- Placed on pipes and cables that will be buried underground so that they can be located when necessary.

- Attached to the ears and other internal and external areas of wild animals to track their migratory habits and other behaviors.

- Produced as temporary security bracelets for entry into concerts and ball games to compensate for inadequate guard coverage.

- Manufactured into laptop computers in such a way that any attempt to remove the tag would render the computer inoperable. Such tagged computers could not easily be removed from business offices and other facilities.

- Expected to be a boon for retailers who deal with product recalls. The number of recalls instituted by the FDA alone rose from 1500 in 1988 to 4500 in 2001.[85]

- Manufactured into food packaging for the purpose of recipe planning and meal preparation. See http://www.inf.ethz.ch/vs/res/proj/rfidchef/.

According to an analysis conducted by the Venture Development Corp. (VDC, Natick, MA), the five fastest-growing application areas for RFID technology are, in descending order: point-of-sale, rental item tracking, baggage handling, real-time location systems, and supply chain management.[86] VDC predicts a sustained annual growth rate of 24% through 2005 and possibly beyond.[87]

Chipless RFID

The RFID tag design specification endorsed by the MIT Auto-ID Center requires an integrated circuit chip. An elementary chipless tag design has been invented by INKODE.[88] INKODE makes a patented passive RFID tag that is composed of microscopic antennas, or filament resonators, called Taggents™, which are manufactured into flexible or rigid paper, cardboard, plastic, glass, rubber, and other materials. The Taggents are smaller than four microns in diameter. INKODE tags can be applied to virtually any surface or can be manufactured directly into paper and other materials (Figure 28). The tags, which are about the size of a postage stamp, cost a fraction of a penny, yet can be read at distances greater than two meters (6.56 feet). The tags are interrogated using low-power readers which use RF energy (Figure 29). Despite their low cost, the tags are, on one hand, durable, with an archival life of more than one hundred years, and, on the other, are "environmentally acceptable." The tags are transparent and are invisible to the unaided eye.

The tags can be created in a purely random fashion, each with its own Electronic Signature™. Each tag has its own identity and responds uniquely to an interrogator. The odds of there being a duplicate configuration is in the range of 1 in 300 billion. INKODE can also produce sequentially numbered or alphanumeric resonator arrays.

The company sells xerographic copier modification systems that will incapacitate a copier if a sheet with an INKODE RF tag is placed anywhere on the glass platen. It makes another that will only copy if it detects the INKODE tag. The company also licenses Safe-to-Shred paper shredders that come in two varieties, one that will not accept paper or other materials which contain INKODE tags and one that will only shred materials that contain the tag. Users can buy

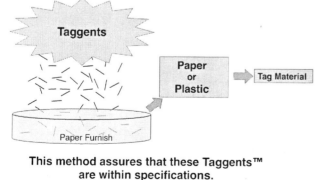

Microscopic Radio Frequency Resonant Dipole Antennas called "Taggents™" (Tag - Agent) are mixed in during the papermaking process. This mix is carefully controlled to assure the customer maximum performance.

Taggents

Paper or Plastic → Tag Material

Paper Furnish

This method assures that these Taggents™ are within specifications.

Figure 28. Taggents can be mixed with the paper making furnish such as pulps and other chemicals, during the manufacturing process. (Image courtesy of INKODE.)

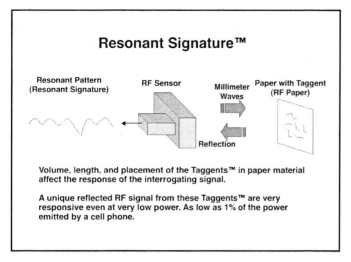

Resonant Signature™

Resonant Pattern (Resonant Signature)   RF Sensor   Millimeter Waves   Paper with Taggent (RF Paper)

Reflection

Volume, length, and placement of the Taggents™ in paper material affect the response of the interrogating signal.

A unique reflected RF signal from these Taggents™ are very responsive even at very low power. As low as 1% of the power emitted by a cell phone.

Figure 29. INKODE Taggents can be mixed directly into paper pulp during the manufacturing process. The unique Resonant Signature that is produced by each finished unit is determined by the volume, length, and placement of the Taggents pattern. (Image courtesy of INKODE.)

INKODE stickers to apply to documents they want to protect or destroy. Detection systems, for R&D labs, libraries, banks, law firms, and other document-control environments, in the form of portal scanners, are available to detect the attempted removal of documents that contain INKODE tags.

Printed Electronics and RFID

Although optical measuring instruments can be used to evaluate and characterize conventional print, the primary analysis of its measure of acceptability is the human eye.[89] Print is a visual product, and its value lies in its capacity to communicate information. Everyone who uses print evaluates it either consciously or subconsciously everyday. It is likely to be acceptable unless it has gross imperfections that draw attention to the process rather than to the content.

The application of traditional printing processes for the production of electronic devices, however, fundamentally alters the print production equation, assigning significantly more variables to the nature of the printed product since it is now an electronic device. Visual inspection is no longer sufficient since circuits cannot be properly judged solely on appearance. Printed electronics can be judged on a gross scale in regard to ink density using a densitometer, provided that readings can be correlated to circuit functions. Perhaps the most critical visual measure will be line resolution, wherein the feature size of the circuits is maintained within acceptable tolerances. Magnification and high-speed video analysis and laser scanning are likely to be helpful in this regard, as well as in measuring ink film thickness.

All of the elements that combine to form a printing system must be considered in light of the requirements imposed for the production of a particular printed item, be it a cereal box or an electronic device. According to Bob Boyes, product marketing manager at Cookson Electronics Equipment, the list consists of the following:

1. *Material to be applied:* This may be a conventional ink, a conductive paste, an adhesive, or another form of coating.

2. *Substrate:* The choice of substrate is likely to be determined by the material that will be deposited on its surface.

3. *Feature size:* What is the smallest feature or critical dimension (CD) that will need to be produced?

4. *Feature shape:* What shape will the feature need to form?

5. *Registration requirements:* How reliably can the pattern be applied from item to item? If multiple patterns are to be applied, can they be held in register?

6. *Technologies available:* What printing technology and methods are best suited to match the specifications?

7. *Quantity to be produced:* Can the required quantity be produced in a reasonable time and at an acceptable cost?

8. *Other process rates:* How will other processes that precede or follow in the manufacture of the product affect overall manufacturing efficiency?

9. *End unit cost requirements:* What are the practical limitations associated with the cost of manufacture to the customer?

10. *Capital expenditure consideration:* Is the process affordable and a good and reasonable investment?

A major driving force behind the development of printed electronics is the objective of developing methods for producing very low-cost RFID tags in massive quantities. The market for such a product would likely be the largest in the history of mankind, accounting for billions per day.

There are several inherent limitations in chip-based RFID tags. These include the fact that silicon fabrication is costly. Also, since the chip size must be small in order to keep the cost low, the antenna must usually be produced as a separate component[90] and the two parts assembled. Given the performance criteria required for many RFID applications, "it is extremely unlikely that these printed tags will ever offer the performance (in terms of range, data rate, anti-collision capabilities, etc.) that will be available in silicon-based RFID. Therefore it is likely that both technologies will coexist, with silicon providing the high-end inventory control and pallet-level tracking, while printed RFID will provide the supermarket shelf RFID."[91]

The printed electronics state of the art is still quite primitive, and much work remains to be done to bring any products, no less extremely low-cost products, to the market. In general, the standard printing processes have yet to be proven capable of producing features small enough to satisfy the needs of the microelectronics industry (see Table D: Applications of Traditional Printing Processes to the Fabrication of Electronics). The main components that are used to fabricate plastic electronics are organic thin film field-effect transistors (FETs), although research is still focused on identifying the materials with the necessary properties to support acceptable transistor performance. According to John Rogers et. al of Lucent Technology, "While the present set of materials are not suitable for printing thin film transistors (TFT) from sequential liquid layers neither can printing presses hold the resolution and registration required for device fabrication. In time, these difficulties may be surpassed and the vision of printing organic devices in a press may come to pass but that promise is, at minimum, a few years away."[92]

Offset Lithography. Given that a typical image-setter or CTP device can image at 2540 dpi, the size of the spot produced is approximately 10 µm wide. There are many on-press variables that will affect the size of the

dot that is ultimately printed, such as the ink characteristics, the blanket surface and condition, the cylinder pressures, the substrate surface, and others. Although the width of the dot and the width of a space (that is, a non-printing dot) are theoretically the same, the printed dot will likely be larger. A single dot can not be seen by the human eye at normal viewing distances, nor can micro-electronic circuit tracings. In terms of the smallest functional printing, Franz Sigg, an RIT senior technologist, reports that "I have done an experiment for a customer and found that a text with a sans serif typeface and all capitals could be printed and read reliably where the letter E was 100 µm high, which means that the nominal width of the arms and spaces are about 20 µm thick. This was on coated paper on a sheetfed press at RIT…100 µm is 4 mils or about the width of a hair."[93]

Screen Printing. The process of screen printing involves a patterned screen mask, holding the image, through which ink is forced by moving a squeegee, called a *doctor blade*, across its surface. The process is additive in nature and is capable of producing lines and spaces as small as 50–75 µm. The process has been used routinely in the manufacture of commercial printed circuit boards, and is, perhaps, the only conventional printing process that has gained a broad level of acceptance in the field of electronics fabrication. One of its chief characteristics is its capability to print a thick layer of ink.

Although the process is sometimes erroneously referred to as "silk screen" printing, most screens today are composed of either polyester or stainless steel. The screen materials, which are also used in a variety of industries for such things as filtration and material reinforcement, are manufactured in a wide variety of weaves or mesh. In general, the mesh plays a major role in determining the resolution of the printed images. The selection of a screen mesh should follow these guidelines:

Printing Process	Smallest Printable Feature	Application
Gravure Offset	50 µm	• Conductor lines on ceramic substrates • Pattern thin-film transistors for low-cost displays
Offset Lithography	25 µm	• Fabrication of capacitors using printed lines
Electrophotography	Not Available	• Pattern transistors and conductors on dielectric materials
Screen Printing	50–75 µm	• Commercial printed circuit boards
Inkjet	10–30 µm	• Presently the dominant experimental method

Table D. Application of traditional printing processes to the fabrication of electronics. Based on information contained in Michel, Bernard et. al, 2001, and other sources.

- The mesh thread diameter determines the minimum line width that can be printed. That width is usually three times the mesh thread diameter.

- The mesh opening determines the maximum size of the print medium (i.e., ink or paste) particles that can be printed. The mesh opening should be at least three times as big as the particulate, which is usually not larger than 5 or 10 μm.[94]

Screen printing is being used in many research labs for producing functional polymer circuits. At the Fraunhofer Research Institute in Germany, for example, researchers have used screen printing to successfully print circuits. According to Fraunhofer's Gerhard Klink, "Once we have mastered this technique, it won't be long before we can implement offset printing processes."[95]

Screen printing, as practiced in typical commercial operations, is susceptible to a wide variety of quality control issues related to the process variables. Unacceptable print images can be caused by a multitude of things, such as: improper squeegee contact, inadequate squeegee blade width, excessive or insufficient squeegee pressure, improper stencil emulsion thickness, improper ink viscosity, dried ink in the screen mesh, poorly made screens, inappropriate screen mesh selection (see Table E: Typical Screen Printing Mesh Sizes), and dozens of other potential problems.

Soft Lithography. Soft lithography, invented by George M. Whitesides,[96] a Harvard University chemistry professor, is somewhat of a misnomer since it does not resemble what is commonly known as lithographic printing.[97] It involves high-resolution patterning methods formed by casting and curing a prepolymer (polydimethyl siloxane, PDMS, also known as silicone rubber) in contact with a patterned photoresist on a molecular scale.

According to Dr. Whitesides, "It may not be a question of plastic-based microelectronics catching up [with silicon], but making something different instead."[98] Processes in this category use elastomer masks, molds, and stamps and are capable of printing features as small as 10 μm. The concept is somewhat reminiscent of rubber-stamp printing (flexography) and could possibly be applied in a wide-format roll-to-roll manufacturing operation. Whitesides' process of microcontact printing is capable of transferring a molecular monolayer of ink to a surface (Figure 30).

The use of self-assembled monolayer (SAM) "inks" for high-resolution patterning is referred to as *nano-transfer printing* (nTP). According to Professor Whitesides, "Nanostructures are fabricated ordinarily using advanced nanolithographic techniques such as e-beam writing, X-ray lithography, and proximal-probe lithography. These techniques are capable of providing very small features, but their development into methods for generating large areas of nanostructures rapidly and at low cost will require some ingenuity…The lack of techniques capable of generating and manufacturing nanostructures rapidly and economically represents a limiting step in the area of nanoscience and nanotechnology…Soft lithography suggests a new conceptual approach to nanomanufacturing: advanced nanolithographic techniques would be used to make masters, and these structures would then be transferred into organic polymers or other materials using procedures such as printing, molding, embossing, or a combination thereof…Currently, our ability to manufacture is limited to devices where small feature size is important but lateral distortions are not: single-level structures such as polarizers and waveguides. The limitations are due to the yet unresolved issues of registration and distortion. Further practical technological uses of these techniques will require further development."[99]

Conventional semiconductor fabrication uses lithography to print circuits onto microchips.[100] This projection process uses masters that are 4× to 5× masks, which are considerably easier to construct than the 1× masks or

Classification	Typical Mesh	Polyester	Stainless Steel
Very heavy deposit, quality of outline not important	Under 40/cm 100/in	21/cm 54/in	31/cm 80/in
Heavy deposit, good definition	40–80/cm 100–200/in	77/cm 195/in	77/cm 200/in
All lettering and illustrations	80–125/cm 200–325/in	120/cm 305/in	125/cm 325/in
Thin deposit, extra-fine detail	125–154/cm 320–400/in	150/cm 380/in	154/cm 400/in

Table E. Typical screen printing mesh sizes. Chart courtesy of DEK USA, Universal SMT Laboratory, P.O. Box 825, Binghamton, NY 13902-0825.

Figure 30. Dr. John Rogers, formerly of Lucent Laboratories and now at the University of Illinois Champaign-Urbana, holds a flexible silicone "printing plate" made by pouring liquid resin over a silicon wafer. The wafer had been imaged using normal microelectronics fabrication methods in a clean room environment. The resulting image master contains the extremely fine features residing on the wafer surface. With the use of molecular inks, the pattern on the plate can be inked and transferred to a plastic sheet by contact printing. This method has been used successfully to produce thin film transistor backplanes. (Photo by author.)

masters required for classic printing and soft lithography. Although the process is expected to enable the "printing" of circuits as small as 0.1 µm wide (or about 1/1000th the width of a human hair), it is expected that Extreme Ultraviolet (EUV) Lithography will make possible circuit lines as small as 0.03 µm (30 nanometers).

Nanotechnology, according to the Institute for the Future, "is the direct manipulation of matter at the atomic or molecular level. As such, it has vast implications for the computer industry."[101] Computer processors that are made using this patterning technology are predicted to be capable of speeds up to 10 GHz in 2007, although nanometer feature sizes will eventually meet limits when trying to process a fraction of an electron.[102] Nonetheless, the process is expected to keep pace with Moore's Law, as postulated by Gordon Moore in 1965, which states that the transistor density of silicon-integrated circuits will double every eighteen months. Moore's second law, which is less known, states that "the cost of building fabrication facilities (or fabs) for electronic circuits based on lithography and subtractive processes increases by a factor of two every generation. The present generation of logic and memory chips are being built in billion-dollar fabs, which means that a fab line for true nanostructures made by current strategies would cost many tens or even hundreds of billions of dollars to construct. On the other hand, additive processes, such as chemical synthesis and self-assembly or guided-assembly techniques, hold the promise of making nanostructures very inexpensively and appear to be necessary for the successful development of nanotechnology."[103]

Gravure. The gravure process has the distinction of having been used to produce the smallest precision printed book in the world, as certified by the Guinness Book of World Records. The Microbook, produced in 2000 by Toppan Printing, measures just 0.95 mm square. It is manually printed and bound.[104]

The gravure process requires a halftone screen to print images, even solids. Using a screen ruling of 150 lpi, the screening pattern has a structure of approximately 160 µm. Due to the rigor of gravure cylinders, extraordinarily long pressruns can be achieved.

Flexography. Flexography is the process that many scientists sometimes refer to as "classic printing," wherein a raised surface is "inked" then brought into contact with a substrate. Newly developed microprinting methods work in a similar way. In most flexographic printing situations the practical controllable printing limit is a 150 line screen, which in a 3% dot area can print a dot that measures approximately 32 µm. The inherent problem with flexography is that minute dot areas cannot withstand the pressure of the process for a sustained period of time and will degrade and disappear.

Letterpress. Letterpress is not used much today. It is speculated, however, that its process capabilities are similar to, and perhaps better than, those of flexography.

Inkjet. The resolution of inkjet printers used in the graphic arts, usually for wide-format work, have a mechanical resolvable addressability of from 360–720 dpi, although some manufacturers claim to have resolutions of greater than 2000 dpi. These higher numbers are suspect since they are sometimes attributable to marketing hype rather than to true device resolvability. In any event the estimated size of the smallest feature is about 70 µm.

The use of inkjet for printing organic transistors necessitates the production of pinhole-free layers to avoid the possibility of the shorting of devices. In addition, electronic devices produced using inkjet will necessarily consist of multiple layers of different materials, introducing the problems of resolution, registration, and bonding. Lab experiments have produced acceptable single-layer organic transistors using an inkjet resolution of 50 µm, and work is being conducted with nanoparticle inks of gold and other metals to form electronic conductors. Inkjet also has potential in the production of OLED displays. According to Professor Paul Calvert of the University of Arizona, "Since the resolution of displays is similar to that of printed paper, inkjet printing should readily lend itself to OLEDs once a wider range of materials and multiple layers become possible."[105]

Seiko Epson Corporation, which itself manufactures inkjet printers, has developed what they call the Micro Liquid Process for fabricating flat panel displays using inkjet printing. Through the use of inkjet they are able to directly pattern a functional liquid material onto a substrate producing an LCD color filter, full-color OLED display, and organic TFTs for electrophoretic displays. The system that they used, which is similar to those used in their high-end inkjet printers, has multi-nozzle print heads that maintain a controlled drop size in excess of 2.5-billion droplets and with an accuracy of better than 15 µm across the surface of the substrate. According to Dr. Tatsuya Shimoda of Epson, "Several devices for flat panel displays have been successfully developed and produced using inkjet printing based on the micro-liquid process content. When mass-produced, these devices will be far more inexpensive than those fabricated by the conventional process. Moreover, the simplified processes and equipment make fabrication facilities very compact and efficient. We can expect a steady stream of new inkjet printing applications to make their way into the area of display fabrication in the future."[106]

Electrostatic Printing. Electronic components have been fabricated successfully, in demonstration projects, using liquid toners and electrostatic processing on a variety of materials, including metal, glass, and high-temperature polyimide.

Standards for Printed Electronics

The need for industry standards is obvious if a technology is to grow, become successful, and be understood and properly applied. For that purpose a working group (P1620) was formed by two individuals from the Motorola Advanced Technology Center, Paul Brazis, Ph.D., and Daniel Gamota, Ph.D., under sponsorship of the Institute of Electrical and Electronics Engineers Standards Association (IEEE-SA). Their first task is "the establishment of standard procedures and reporting standards for the characterization of organic field-effect transistors...The effect of storage and testing environment is of particular concern, as environmental effects have been widely shown to have a significant effect on electrical performance...The first standards initiative is intended to formalize future reporting practices in the literature and between organizations. Subsequent initiatives will address other areas, including design tools, standard design practices, reliability testing, and product operation standards."[107] Their tentative timetables for organic and molecular electronics are shown in Table F and Table G.

Inks for Printing Electronic Structures

The application of traditional printing processes and equipment for the fabrication of electronic devices is heavily dependent upon advances in material science that will produce the inks that form electronic circuits and components and the substrates onto which they are printed. Much is known about the conventional printing inks and several established test methods are in place to assess the physical, chemical, visual, and electrical properties of printing inks.[108] Dan Lawrence, manager of the Print as Manufacture division of Flint Ink, has identified the four categories of test methods proven useful for testing conventional printing inks, and of potential value for conductive inks used to print electronics (Table H: Test Methods Used for the Analysis of Conventional Printing Inks).

Several companies produce inks either that are being used, or are likely to be used, on conventional printing presses to produce some element of an electronic device.

Flint Ink.[109] Flint Ink, founded in 1920 and the largest privately owned printing ink manufacturer in the world, opened a new conductive and advanced ink development and resource center in the fall of 2003 near its Global Research and Development Center in Ann Arbor, MI. The center includes a dedicated laboratory, controlled pressroom environment, and conference and display areas. They have negotiated several business and professional relationships and partnerships that allow them to extend the reach of their in-house operations.[110] Areas of research and development include RFID, printed electronics, intelligent packaging, lighting, and printed displays.

Flint defines conductive inks as "specially prepared suspensions of finely dispersed conductive particles (most commonly silver and/or carbon) in a variety of resin systems. The inks are used to produce conductive patterns on flexible and rigid substrates."[111] The images that are formed from the inks are used to print conductive tracks for various electronic devices and components, including:

- Membrane switches
- RFID antennae
- Circuit components
- Printed wiring boards
- Intelligent packaging

Conductive inks are available for printing by flexography, gravure, lithography and screen printing, and can be printed on most types of paper, paperboard, polyester, treated polyester, and vinyl. The inks are available in water- or solvent-based formulations, and some formulations may be cured at room temperature. The water-based inks are compatible with most substrates and blan-

H1Y2003	H2Y2003	H1Y2004	H2Y2004	H1Y2005
Device Characterization	Circuit Characterization	Manufacturing Characterization	Reliability Testing	Wireless Protocols Interfaces
		Circuit Design Tools	Audio Protocols Interfaces	
		Display Protocols Interfaces		

Table F. Tentative timeline for standards initiatives—Organic electronics (H = half)

H1Y2004	H2Y2004	H1Y2005	H2Y2005	H1Y2006
Device Characterization	Circuit Characterization	Manufacturing Characterization	Reliability Testing	
		Circuit Design Tools	Wireless Protocols Interfaces	
		Microprocessing Protocols Interfaces		

Table G: Tentative timeline for standards initiatives—Molecular electronics.

Physical	Chemical	Visual	Electrical
processes that yield an analysis of the types of chemicals and chemical bonds within an ink.	processes that yield an analysis of the types of chemicals and chemical within an ink.	the appearance to the eye or an optical measurement tool.	measurements that can be used to understand antistatic properties and to promote ink transfer in the presence of large electric fields.
Surface Tension: the compatibility of inks and substrates.		Mottle: a measure of the uniformity of the appearance of a uniformly printed area.	
Rheology: the study of the deformation and flow of materials under different pressures, rates of shear, temperatures, and amplitudes of oscillation.		Optical Density: a measurement of the intensity, or level of contrast, of a given color.	
Mileage: a measure of the number of satisfactory prints that can be formed with a given amount of ink.		Spectrophotometry: the quantification of color reflected from a printed page using a standard light source.	
Film Thickness: a measure of the ink layer as determined by the printing process, substrate, press conditions, and ink properties.		Optical Microscopy: a reading of surface detail well beyond observable by the unaided eye.	
Rub Resistance: a measure of the structural integrity of the printed surface during its useful lifetime.		Electron Microscopy: a view with greater magnification and depth of field than optical methods.	
Adhesion: a measure of the physical strength of printed ink structures on a substrate.			

Table H. Test methods used for the analysis of conventional printing inks.

kets and contain no potentially harmful solvents or volatile organic compound (VOC) emissions.

In addition to producing conductive inks, Flint Ink, and others, manufacture *seed inks*. Seed inks are used to print circuit patterns onto which a layer of copper will be plated. The process is additive in that the ink acts as a base between the plated metal and the substrate. The plated copper circuits can be produced lithographically and applied to the high-speed production of smart cards and similar kinds of circuitry.

Parelec.[112] Parelec, which has a business arrangement with Flint Ink, makes Parmod VLT (very low temperature) conductive inks and pastes that can be printed on polyimide, polyester, or paper using either sheetfed or web presses. It has advantages over polymer thick film inks in that its conductivity is ten times higher, producing an antenna with greater range, and not only can it be soldered but it also can act as a lead-free solder. When cured at approximately 135–150°C for two minutes, the material converts to pure metal to form electronic circuits that are useful for fabricating RFID tags, membrane switches, flexible circuits, and high-density interconnect applications. Parelec anticipates that its inks will be adaptable for printing thin film transistor arrays, capacitors, displays, and other low-cost electronic devices.

Parmod can be formulated as an ink, paste, or toner composed of a mixture of one or more powders with a reactive organic medium (ROM). It is capable of printing a resolution of 150 μm (6 mil) lines and spaces, with a thickness of from 1 to 50 μm (2 mil).

Acheson Colloids Company.[113] Acheson Colloids Company has a long history, extending more than fifty years, in producing carbon, graphite, silver, and silver-coated copper inks. Silver inks have been sold in recent years for printing antennas for RFID and smart card applications. The Acheson Electrodag® 461SS is a conductive silver pigment-based ink that is screen printable and cures in five minutes at 250°F. The ink is formulated for printing on polyester and consists of a thermoplastic resin with "very finely divided silver particles" in dispersion.

Dow COMMOTION.[114] Scientists at The Dow Chemical Company have developed a reflective display technology that can be produced using an ink formulation composed of commercially available components, that can be applied using conventional sheetfed screen printing processes. As such, COMMOTION can be considered a "fabless display company," producing displays without the high costs and long lead times required to construct a conventional display fabrication facility. The innovative technology, developed over the last three years, enables the high-volume production of thin, flexible, low-cost electronic displays for smart cards, smart

active labels, and eventually novelty and promotional applications.

The COMMOTION technology is centered around a number of proprietary electrochromic inks that respond to a low-power electrical charge (1.2 to 2.5 volts) by changing color. As the technology matures it is expected to move from sheetfed to web-based screen printing, and eventually to flexography or gravure. The amount of information that can be conveyed and the resolution of the image are engineered to address specific display applications. Although the technology does not support video speed, pixels can be switched at a rate of 250 msec. A COMMOTION display can cycle through 50,000 to 500,000 pixel activations during its lifetime, and a display is estimated to have a shelf life of more than three years. Initially, COMMOTION will manufacture and sell display components.

The COMMOTION production process consists of five steps:

1. The display backplane circuit is printed on a PET plastic film using commercially available conductive inks and dielectrics.

2. The top-plane is printed as a conductive ring and dielectric pattern onto commercially available ITO-coated PET film. The top-plane may also be used to carry an art mask or graphic overlay.

3. The display elements are screen printed using COMMOTION electrochromic ink across the transparent top electrode (ITO) surface.

4. The layers are sealed using a printed or pressure-sensitive adhesive and then laminated.

5. The display device is cut using a die or laser cutting process and packaged as a finished good.

The first commercial product produced using COMMOTION technology was a Valentine's Day card for the British retailer, Marks & Spencer (Figure 31). The animated greeting card, manufactured in December 2002, was sold in February 2003 at a limited number of test sites and at a cost of about £3 ($4.70).

The Printed Antenna Project at RIT

A multidisciplinary research project was conducted at RIT during the summer of 2003 to investigate the potential for printing RFID antennas using flexography. Most of the previous work done in regard to printing RFID antennas has used screen printing technology. Flexog-

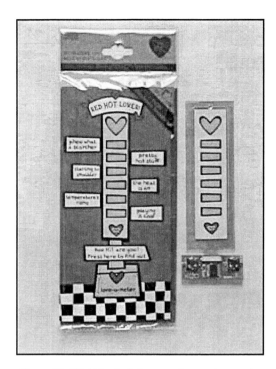

Figure 31. This Valentine's Day novelty greeting card, which sold in limited distribution in early 2003, is the first commercial implementation of the Dow COMMOTION display process. The packaged card is shown on the left and the display component and driver electronics are shown on the right. (Photo courtesy of Dow COMMOTION.)

substrates. The initial testing involved the selection of substrates based upon a variety of factors, particularly thermal stability. Other factors considered were dimensional stability, availability, cost, and electric and magnetic properties. Although both paper and plastic substrates were examined, the results were found to be best for paper substrates, particularly coated paper.

One of the findings was that visual inspection is not a good predictor of electrical performance. Some of the prints that were produced were visually acceptable but did not perform well electrically. Small gaps of ink, while not noticeable to the eye (but observable microscopically), can completely negate electrical continuity. The project leader, Dr. Bruce Kahn, devised a visual scanning process that reveals areas that did not receive sufficient ink coverage, as well as areas which should not have received any.

The printed test antennas were evaluated using a variety of methods including optical microscopy, scanning electron microscopy, resistance measurements, profilometry, and network analysis.

At the conclusion of the project the team was able to print RFID antennas having sheet resistivities of 83 mW/ with line heights of ~6 mm. They achieved >80% radiation efficiency at the peak resonance frequency. Furthermore, the team achieved electrically continuous coatings over >50 cm long with line widths as thin as 200 μm. The project was considered a success and may be the beginning of a long-term research commitment.

raphy has the advantage that it can be applied for high-volume printing. The project was a collaborative effort involving RIT's School of Print Media and the Imaging and Photographic Technology, Materials Science and Engineering, and Electrical Engineering departments.

An IGT F1 Printability Tester located in RIT's Printing Applications Lab (PAL) was used as a mechanism to investigate the performance characteristics of printed antennas in regard to a variety of printing process parameters (Figure 32). The investigation allowed for the optimization of some of the process parameters using very small quantities of ink. The study team used commercially available conductive inks from several manufacturers, but primarily focused on a new ink formulation developed by Parelec, Inc.

The Parelec ink formulation is unique in that after it is cured, it produces features that are completely metallic, although quite porous. Essentially, the curing process removes all of the organic material, leaving only metal. The curing temperature for this ink is relatively high (150°C), but it is compatible with a number of different

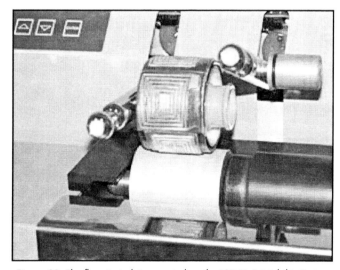

Figure 32. The flexo test plate mounted on the IGT F1 Printability Tester. The antenna image, seen on the plate, was designed by Michael Seymour, a second-year RIT electrical engineering graduate student. Michael worked under the co-direction of RIT Professors Bruce Kahn and Jayanti Venkataraman.

Organic Semiconductor Inks

The markets for printed electronics are huge, and are a reflection of what may be the next implementation of the Internet: an Internet of Things, sometimes referred to as The Product Internet or T2T.[115] The Internet of Things consists of intelligent objects, trillions of them, in the physical environment that can communicate and form a real-time network of things. Endowing everyday objects with computer capabilities has already occurred, with such things as smart TVs that record programs based on perceived viewer preferences, car navigation systems that calculate routes based on the kind of driving routes that a driver likes, wireless telephones that can access Web-based information, and much more. The world that printed electronics will bring will enable the incorporation of computer logic into virtually everything that can benefit from it.

The practicality of printed electronics relies primarily on the development of inks that can be used to create semiconductor devices using traditional printing processes. The most popular forms of organic semiconductor inks are electrically active oligomers, polymers, and small molecules in solution and in suspension. Laboratory work reported by TAGA suggests that these inks can be applied to a variety of substrates that have been used for traditional printing, such as paper and polyester. There are obvious and compelling reasons to want to fabricate electronic devices using high-speed printing presses as opposed to traditional silicon fabrication processes. These include:

- a substantial price differential in equipping a printing shop compared to building a semiconductor fabrication facility. While a sophisticated printing plant would cost in the millions of dollars, a modern fab would cost in the billions.

- a significant differential in the cost of labor to manage and operate the plants

- a significantly greater volume of output.

There are many significant problems inherent in printing electronics using traditional methods. These include:

- the necessity to refine the materials for optimum performance

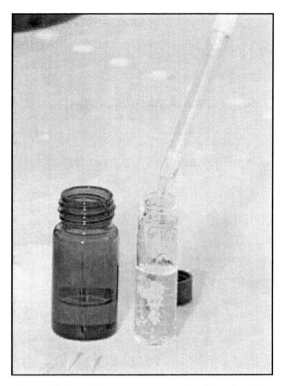

Figure 33. The inkjet printing process is solution-based. Here, the semiconductor material is being dissolved in solution. (Photo courtesy of Plastic Logic, ©2003, Plastic Logic, Cambridge.)

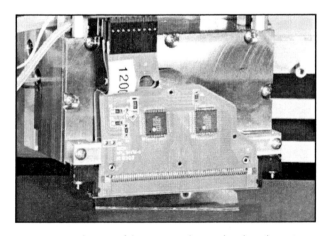

Figure 34. A close-up of the 256-nozzle print head used to print Plastic Logic electronics. (Photo courtesy of Plastic Logic, ©2003, Plastic Logic, Cambridge.)

- the need to develop testing and control processes and procedures for producing zero defects in a roll-to-roll operation or for marking bad product as it is produced

- ensuring accurate registration and in-line testing

- controlling the ambient environment within the tolerances required by the materials

- acquiring the infrastructure to convert rolls of printed features into finished products.

Polymer-Based Electronics

Plastic Logic.[116] Plastic Logic (see PICRM-2002-01, page 50) is in the formative stage of commercializing the production of solution-based polymer-based electronics (Figure 33) using an inkjet printing process (Figure 34). From the beginning of 2002 to mid-2003 the company raised $17 million in venture funding and grew from fifteen to forty-five employees. Full commercial implemen-

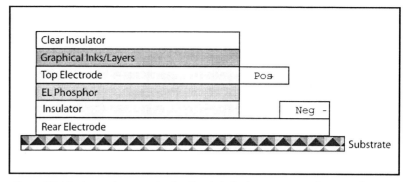

Figure 36. The layers that comprise the Crosslink display process can be printed on plastic, fabrics, glass, and metals and can be vacuum formed onto a mold.

tation is still probably three or more years away. Polymer-based electronics can be used in place of chip-based RFID tags and offer the feasibility of producing an entirely printed RFID tag consisting of the controller and antenna. Although polymer-based electronics are not likely to provide the speed, rigor, or storage capacity of silicon, they can be applied in areas where those characteristics are not mission-critical.

The production of logic applications, such as RFID and smart labels, is one of two core areas of development work at Plastic Logic, the other being displays. According to Cranch Lamble, spokesman for Plastic Logic, "The first commercial application for the technology is likely to be in flat panel displays." The company has successfully printed backplanes for liquid crystal (Figure 35) and Gryicon's Smart Paper display media that were displayed at the Society for Information Display in May 2003.

The near-term (12–18 months) plan is to increase display sizes to larger formats and initiate work on flexible substrates. "The advantages of the Plastic Logic approach (low-temp hence flexible substrates, large area, low cost, high-voltage capable, highly customizable) lend themselves to e-Paper and we will continue to work with e-Paper companies to combine our technology with theirs. The prospect of our technology has generated significant interest from both e-Paper and other display companies…Suffice to say that we believe the long term market for Plastic Electronics to be huge…In terms of rollout, this will firm up over the next 12 months, but I envisage 2–3 years before first product (we are at the experimental device stage and then have to move to full prototypes, then alpha and beta product trials before full rollout)," says Lamble.[117]

Crosslink Polymer Research.[118] Crosslink Polymer Research has developed a printable polymer light emission system (Figure 36) that can be applied to a number of surfaces, including plastic, metal, and textiles, using standard screen printing equipment (Figure 37). Their

Figure 35. Plastic Logic's 2-in. liquid crystal demonstrator device showing 80x60 pixels. (Photo courtesy of Plastic Logic, ©2003, Plastic Logic, Cambridge.)

Figure 37. This is one of the screen printing presses used by Crosslink to produce their light-emissive displays for use in advertising, security, safety signage, etc. The process operates in an ambient environment with no vacuum sputtering chambers, clean rooms, or spin coating, which are typical of some display technologies. (Photo courtesy of Crosslink Polymer Research, used with permission.)

Figure 38. An example of a sign manufactured by Crosslink Polymer Research that shows its appearance without power (A) and with power (B). The estimated display life of such a sign is about four years on a cycle mode (i.e., not powered constantly). (Photo courtesy of Crosslink Polymer Research, used with permission.)

textile process can be printed onto a variety of fabrics. The process uses a combination of inks, with both organic and inorganic components, some of which are electrically conductive. By combining inks in the proper amounts and construction, more than twenty colors have been developed, in addition to the four basic process colors.

When connected to an AC power source the device illuminates. By using a programmable controller, multiple lighted zones with multiple colors can be designed to create a combination of light and movement (Figure 38). With the proper combination of ink and substrates, the device is not affected by folding or bending. The displays have an expected life of from three to five years, which varies depending on temperature, humidity, and usage.[119] The process supports the application of illumination to large areas, and printed sheets on a substrate such as

polycarbonate can be thermally formed to conform to various shapes, such as bicycle helmets. The application of displays to clothing is likely to become commonplace (Figure 39). In addition to illumination in the visible spectrum, illumination in the NIR region can be achieved, enabling usage in additional applications, including multiple military uses.

Printed Electronics: Materials

Paper is the largest surface ever manufactured by man. It continues to be applied in new ways and will likely be

Figure 39 . The Hammacher Schlemmer Messaging Hat contains a programmable LCD display that can store up to ten messages with up to 250 characters per message. The messages can be selected individually, or the user can opt to have all ten messages scroll continuously. Input and display is controlled by the use of four buttons on the top of the unit. The cotton hat is available in khaki or black, in a single size that fits most, for $24.95. Although this hat has a detachable display unit, a new generation of clothing will incorporate display technology directly in its fabric. (Photo by author.)

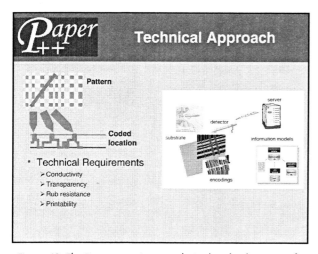

Figure 40. The Paper++ project was devised to develop ways of seamlessly linking content printed on paper to information stored on a computer. (Image courtesy of Paper++.)

used to carry electronic components which will be printed on its surface.

Paper++.[120] In England, a three-year (2001–2003) project is underway called Paper++. The objective of the research is to develop ways of bridging the gap between paper and "electronic domains." The main way by which this is being accomplished is through the use of printing techniques which use invisible conductive inks (Figure 40). Invisible patterns are printed that can be sensed by a special electronic wand. The information sensed by the wand serves as a conduit between the content on the paper and content stored on a computer (Figure 41).

According to Paul Luff, director of the project, "At its simplest, this allows a child reading a book to use a wand to call up sounds associated with a particular image or word. Alternately, a student reading a textbook can use the wand to retrieve related auto-video materials, articles or interactive demonstrations." The elements necessary for enabling the electronic conduit from paper are:

- The paper surface which is printed both with human-readable content and a pattern of invisible lines composed of conductive ink.

- The conductive ink which forms the pattern.

- An encoded pattern that can be properly detected.

- A reader or detector that can sense the pattern.

- A means of mapping the printed pattern on paper to computer resources.

Agfa Orgacon.[121] The workability of printed electronics is based primarily on the use of the right materials applied to the right process. Although much work has been directed toward the development of inks and liquid polymers, the selection of the substrate is equally significant. Agfa has developed a line of films called Orgacon™ that are coated, reel to reel, with a layer of conducting polymers. The coating is composed of PEDOT (polyethylene-dioxithiophene) which is a transparent conductive polymer that can be used as an alternative to ITO (indium-tin oxide). Unlike ITO it is fully flexible, and stable to water, oxygen, and many solvents. The films are electrically patternable and are provided with a uniform conductive coating. A pattern is printed on the film in the areas where they are not to be conductive.

Agfa also makes a transparent conductive screen printing paste called Orgacon™ EL which is based on waterborne conductive polymers. It is used to print transparent electrodes on a variety of surfaces. After the paste has dried it can be overprinted using almost any standard graphic arts ink.

PAELLA.[122] PAELLA (Paper Electronics Low-cost Applications) is an R&D effort started in 1998 and funded by Agfa-Gevaert, Itab, M-Real, SCA, Stora Enso, Tetra Pak, and Vinnova. The project, which has as its objective the printing of low-cost electronics, using both metal and organic conducting lines, on paper at high-speed, is administered by the Acreo Institute in Sweden. They are experimenting with offset, inkjet, screen printing, and dry phase deposition to develop reel-to-reel conversion of webs of paper into electronic devices such as sensors, tags, and displays. Although the electronic

Figure 41. Two young children collaborate on a lesson printed using Paper++ technology. Their use of the electronic wand on the printed images in their lesson book provides interactivity and the display of multimedia content on the connected computer. (Image courtesy of Paper++.)

Figure 42. The flexible, low-cost Power Paper energy cell can be produced in virtually any form factor, including round, as shown in the insert. (Image reprinted with permission from Power Paper.)

devices that they produce, both active and passive, will necessarily be slow compared to silicon fabrication, it is expected that they will also work to develop the market for such electronics. It is believed that whatever processes prove successful on paper can also be used on plastic substrates.

The printing of metal lines for circuitry has been achieved through the development of "a method for dry phase patterning of aluminum foil laminates."[123] The process has yielded patterns from 1 to 20 µm thick on paper or polyester. Organic conducting lines have been printed, using flexo, offset, screen, and plotter printing, producing film thicknesses in the range of 1 to 5 µm.

Power Paper.[124] Power Paper, founded in 1997, has perfected a printable energy cell that is extremely thin (less than 0.5 mm), flexible, disposable, and environmentally friendly (Figure 42). Although the batteries have been applied in a number of applications, including the delivery of cosmetic facial treatments (PowerCosmetics) and as the power for promotional items, the company has also incorporated the technology into a Smart Active Label which they have developed as part of their PowerID™ Division. These smart RFID tags enable total asset visibility (TAV) by virtue of the power that is provided by the Power Paper energy source (Figure 43). Their Smart Active Label has a range of up to 100 m and has read/write capabilities. The power cells, and the PowerID™ smart labels, can

be manufactured in virtually any size and shape using a roll-to-roll manufacturing process.

The PowerID™ RFID labels are produced using a low-cost web screen printing process that is fully automated. The process is sufficiently flexible to provide for the design and manufacture of labels that can conform to almost any material surface and package shape required in virtually any industry. At end-of-life the labels may be disposed of without restriction as they contain no caustic or toxic chemicals.

The Power Paper battery is printed as a thin, flexible continuous web using proprietary inks. According to the company: "Power Paper cells are composed of zinc and manganese dioxide based cathode and anode layers fabricated from proprietary ink-like materials that can be printed, pasted, or laminated onto virtually any substrate, including specialty papers. The cathode and anode are produced as different mixes of ink so that the combination of the two creates a 1.5-volt battery that is thin and flexible. Power Paper's energy cells are produced by printing the ink cathode and anode on a thin and flexible substrate. Unlike conventional batteries, the Company's power source does not require casing. The battery can be coupled into any type of inlay usually used in RFID labels."(See Figure 44).[125]

Power Paper batteries have the following specifications:

- Thickness: 0.5 mm.

- Hard case (metal) sealing is not necessary, therefore the batteries can be formed into any size or shape.

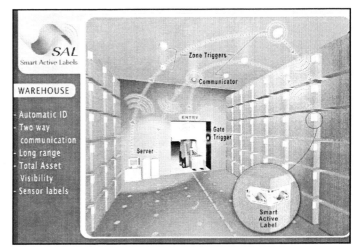

Figure 43. The PowerID™Plus System enables a complete total asset visibility environment. (Image reprinted with permission from Power Paper.)

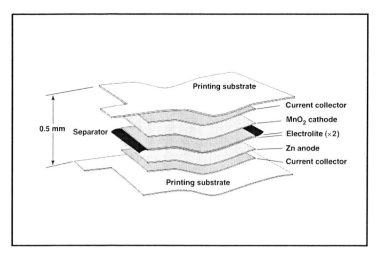

Figure 44. The multiple printed layers that comprise the Paper Power energy cell. (Image reprinted with permission from Power Paper.)

- Very low cost (pennies per battery).

- Disposable as a non-hazardous waste; safe and non-toxic.

- Capacity of 2.5mAh/sq. cm; 1.5-volt battery.

- Shelf life of approximately three years.

- Remains at almost full power before becoming depleted.

- Produced using mass production printing process.

The Power Paper company has developed a production line that is capable of producing hundreds of millions of batteries annually (Figure 45). In addition they license their process to others.[126] The manufacturing steps consist of applying layers of the proprietary inks, drying them, and then laminating them. Typically the printing is accomplished using a screen process, although the "inks" can be applied as paste using "standard thick-film printing processes." The printed batteries can be used for a variety of purposes and sold to OEMs for integration in their products. In addition, Power Paper's roll-to-roll production line enables the inclusion of batteries (35×35-mm) directly into the inlay of an RFID label.

Printed Electronics Forces at Play

Although no one can accurately predict how the nascent printed electronics industry will develop (see Figure 46), here are some observations concerning the forces that are likely to be at play:

Principal Stakeholders. It is likely that developments in the field of printed electronics will continue to be driven by interest from the printing industry for new markets and higher profit margin products and by the electronics industry, interested in lower manufacturing costs, cheaper fabrication facilities, and the potentially insatiable market enabled by the Internet of Things. Each industry has sufficient technical capabilities and expertise, and process control and monitoring strengths, to ensure that they can remain focused on the development of this highly lucrative technology that is not only certain to create new markets but also is likely to change the face of everyday life. These two industries need to work together to a far greater extent than is presently occurring. In addition, the printing industry needs to recognize the potentially enormous impact of this technology and take a major role in its development.

The manufacture of printed electronics components and devices will consist of two distinct production methods—one founded in the commercial printing industry, utilizing conventional printing processes, and the other developed in the electronics fabrication industry, using new printing methods and processes. Although these new printing methods and processes will likely implement higher quality standards and more exacting tolerances than achievable on commercial presses, the cost of building fabrication facilities will be a fraction of what is

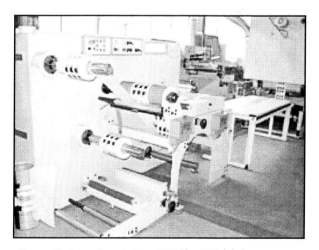

Figure 45. Power Paper's PowerID™ Plus RFID labels are produced in a roll-to-roll manufacturing line. The steps include: loading and threading the substrate, printing or etching the antenna, printing the battery, placing the IC components (flip chip), laminating the layers, and converting to a finished form. RFID tags which have an energy source can improve their reading range from 3 to 100 times.

required for silicon chip manufacture and will therefore encourage significant investments.

It is beyond the scope of this report to draw in-depth comparisons between these two industries; however, based on observations of the relatively slow adoption rates for new technologies in the printing industry, there is cause for concern that this new, potentially enormous opportunity will not be adequately pursued and properly exploited. The electronics industry, on the other hand, is noted for its rapid technological developments and aggressive product development schedules.

Silicon State. The low-cost manufacture of silicon chips will ensure their continued use, in some form, even as the printing of integrated circuits matures. The infrastructure to support chip placement into or onto paper or other substrates will remain a significant cost, as well as a technological challenge. Highly specialized machinery from companies like Bielomatik (http://www.bielomatik-inc.com) and Matrics (http://www.matrics.com) will be increasingly important in satisfying this need. In addition, there will be significant period, of up to twenty years or more, in which printed electronics will include hybrid systems that incorporate silicon chips.

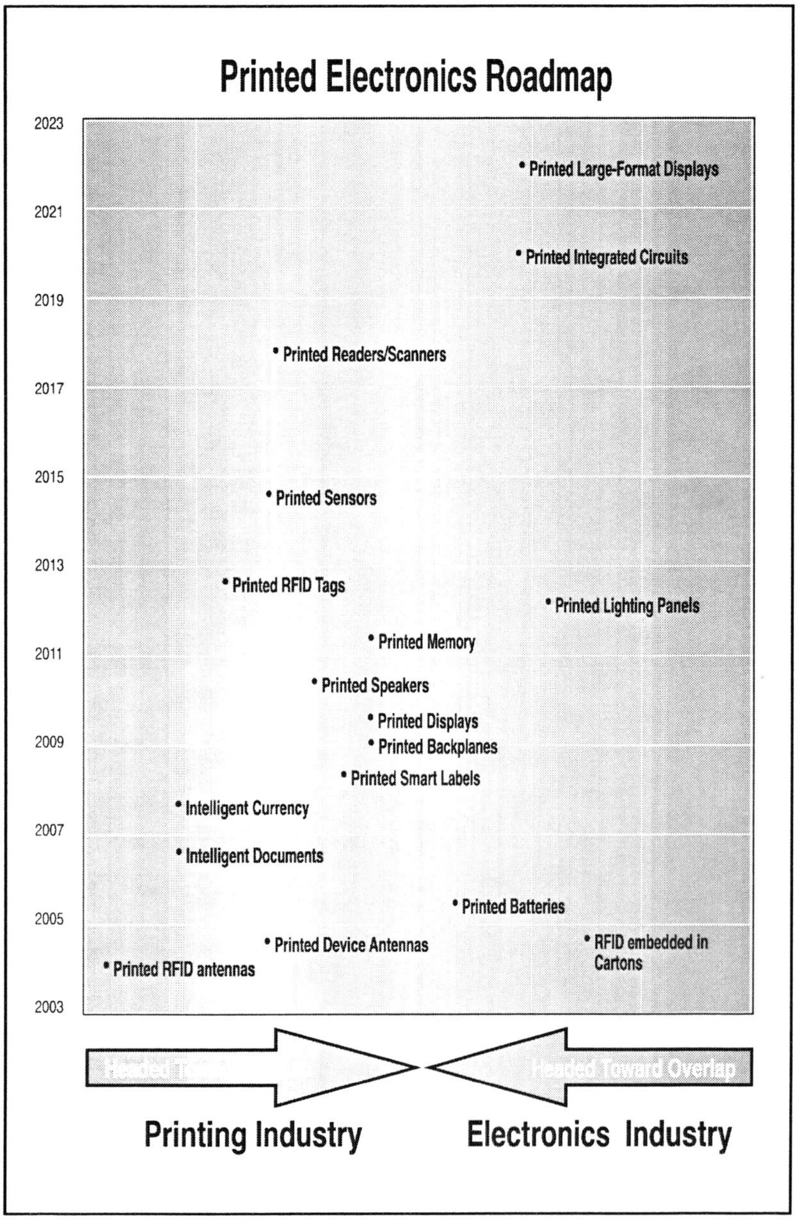

Market Segmentation. There will be a clear division of the printed electronics market into at least two segments: established businesses and new entrants. This will occur both in the commercial printing and the electronic component and fabrication markets. That is to say that there will be one segment characterized by established printers who retrofit their presses and processes, one characterized by new printing industry entrants who build businesses using new conventional presses or "new category" presses, a third composed of established electronics components manufacturers who enter the market to extend their product lines, and the fourth composed of new electronics components manufacturers who utilize new printing methods to enable new products.

Materials Producers. Materials producers, mainly ink, paper, plastic, and chemical manufacturers, will play increasingly more important roles in the field of printed electronics and are likely to work together, not only on the compatibility of their products and the fabrication of goods that contain electronic elements and properties, but also on the development of new classes of materials that will simplify the manufacture of exceptionally low-cost electronic devices.

Electronics Printing Presses. Partnerships are likely to be formed between large established electronics companies and major printing press manufacturers for the creation of the first of several new generations of "printing presses" that print electronic components and devices roll-to-roll. These presses will be the major

Printed Electronics Roadmap

Figure 46. The cross influence of the printing and electronics industries will likely produce an impressive array of low-cost, intelligent devices that will infiltrate nearly every aspect of everyday life.

elements in highly automated manufacturing lines that will start with a roll of blank substrate at one end and produce finished goods at the other.

R&D. Research and development is underway at many private, public, and corporate sites. This field of work includes significant investments at universities and research institutes, government research labs, corporate R&D departments, technology start-ups, independent inventor laboratories, and many others. Such work is likely to have a disruptive effect on what seems to be likely to unfold from today's vantage point.

Spinoffs. Spinoffs are likely to be generated from all of the sectors that have development efforts underway in printed electronics manufacture. While most of these are likely to serve very narrow niche markets, others may open completely new marketplace opportunities that cross into unanticipated realms as diverse as food production, automotive parts, or theme park rides.

Ubiquitous Computing and Society. The massive proliferation of electronics and computing into the fabric of everyday life will not occur unless it is something that is valued by the people who may use it.[127] Resistance to sensory and monitoring devices is already apparent, as are issues related to privacy, ethics, freedom of movement, and fundamental human rights. Although these issues may not stand in the way of developing low-cost printed electronics technology, they will certainly have an impact on its applications and use.

THE SURVEY OF THE FUTURE FOR RFID TAGGING

In the spring of 2003 a survey was drafted composed of questions related to the future of RFID tagging technology and the application of conventional printing methods as an enabling technology. The draft was sent to the partners of the Printing Industry Center at RIT for review, and suggestions and recommendations were incorporated into the final survey instrument (see Appendix: Survey Instrument).

The survey was originally conceived for distribution exclusively to experts in the RFID industry. At the suggestion of one of the Printing Industry Center partners, the survey was also sent to a group of the 99 label printers who are a part of the panel of 643 printers who comprise the standing panel used by the Printing Industry Center for its surveys. The logic was to compare the responses from the two groups: the RFID experts and the label printers. The results from the label printer group was inconclusive, and of the small return of 17 responses, four of them contained comments that clearly showed that the respondents were unfamiliar with the technology and their input was, therefore, of questionable

value. In addition, two of the surveys were returned blank. Here are the comments from the group of four:

- You need to realize that I have very limited knowledge on the above matters.

- No experiences.

- I am not capable of responding to these questions, as RFID tags and consumer product labels are not product or service offerings that we currently provide, or are looking to provide, to our customer base. Consequently, I do not possess the product knowledge.

- I don't know enough about the production of RFID tags at this point to know what will be needed to produce them in a commercial printing establishment. The technology may require paper with an RFID chip embedded in the stock.

In addition, four label printers who did not feel qualified to respond at all to the survey sent email to express their regrets at being unable to provide input. Their comments were:

- I'm sorry; I don't have extensive knowledge in RFID to give you an accurate opinion regarding your questionnaire. Although, I believe the RFID tag is less of a challenge itself than the development of the infrastructure to support its capabilities.

- Sorry. We are not into RFID, and are not knowledgeable in it.

- We are not familiar with the RFID technology. But we would like to find out more about it.

- I don't know enough about this subject to answer your survey.

The poor showing by the label printer group made their survey results statistically unusable; however, the preponderance of comments expressing a lack of knowledge or understanding of RFID technology suggests that there is a strong need for industry education in this area. That finding should be of benefit and make the distribution of this report valuable to printers in general and to label printers in particular, who are likely to be most affected by RFID technology.

The second group of respondents were those who are experts, or are involved in an active capacity with

RFID technology. This group consists of the following components:

- 50 individuals in the author's personal database who are known to be experts in the field and who are known to the author through meetings or email correspondence.

- 4000 readers of the weekly edition of the *RFID Journal* newsletter. The journal editor, Mark Roberti, kindly offered to run an item about the survey in their July 24, 2003, issue.

- >100 members of the worldwide offices of the MIT Auto-ID Center. The Center's director, Sanjay Sarma, kindly offered to distribute the survey to all of his professional colleagues working at centers around the world.

There were 52 responses to the survey as of August 1, 2003, when the survey period ended. Here are the results of the survey:

Survey Question 1: RFID tags are likely to replace UPC bar codes on the majority of consumer goods in…

3–5 years	8
6–10 years	20
11–15 years	12
16–20 years	4
21 or more years	3
Never	5

Question Rationale: There is significant evidence to suggest that RFID tags will gradually replace the ubiquitous UPC bar code on consumer goods…it is only a question of when. The MIT Auto-ID is establishing the infrastructure and the supporting technology that is likely to be applied internationally to make this occur. Its implementation will be based on agreement on the elements that comprise the closed-loop RFID-sensing system; the establishment of an infrastructure to manufacture and supply RFID tags in sufficient quantities, and at an acceptable cost; the availability of affordable readers and other hardware and support components; the buy-in of the majority of goods manufacturers, suppliers, and wholesalers, and retailers; and, of course, acceptance by the buying public.

Interpretation of Results: A majority of the respondents (85%) agree that the RFID revolution will occur within the next twenty years. Only 10% believe that

RFID tags will never replace UPC bar codes. Although not stated in the question, it is likely that there will be a long transition period in which both UPC bar codes and RFID tags will be co-applied to products. This will ensure that those retailers, and others in the supply chain, who are not RFID-enabled, will be able to scan the products.

Survey Question 2: In order for RFID tags to become prevalent on consumer goods, their total cost of production must be:

Less than 10 cents	8
Less than 5 cents	21
Less than 1 cent	22
No Response	1

Question Rationale: Perhaps the most critical element in establishing a widespread RFID tag presence is a purely economic one. It is estimated that more than five billion UPC-bar-coded items are scanned daily. Replacing those bar codes with RFID tags is only practical if the tag costs are sufficiently low. The UPC bar code, aside from taking up packaging real estate, essentially rides for free. The MIT Auto-ID Center has made a strong case for a chip-based RFID tag that costs five cents or less.

Interpretation of Results: 83% of the respondents agree with the five-cents-or-less (including less than one cent) target cost which has been established by the MIT Auto-ID Center. 42% believe that RFID tags must cost less than one cent in order for them to be included on most consumer goods. Certainly the lower the cost of the tags, the more likely that they will be used, and in the case of lower-cost items such as candy bars and pocket combs, the cost of the tag must be negligible.

Survey Question 3: Silicon chip-based RFID tags will remain the primary form of tag production for:

3–5 years	17
6–10 years	18
11–15 years	11
16–20 years	2
21 or more yrs	3
No Response	1

Question Rationale: The RFID tag infrastructure that is being proposed by the MIT Auto-ID Center is based on a chip-based RFID tag that is capable of storing a 96-bit Electronic Product Code that is unique for each item on which it is affixed. The reliance on the chip component may impact the cost of the tag as well as the eventual migration to a totally printed RFID tag.

Interpretation of Results: A majority of respondents (88%) reported that the dependency on a physical chip, as a component of an RFID tag, is likely to subside in fifteen or fewer years. The absence of the chip component will eliminate production steps, lower overall tag cost, and likely enable a totally printed RFID tag.

Survey Question 4: Printed RFID antennas (used with a silicon-based RFID chip) will be the primary antenna format in:

3–5 years	27
6–10 years	16
11–15 years	4
16–20 years	0
21 or more years	3
Never	1
No Response	1

Question Rationale: The use of conductive inks from a variety of manufacturers have been proven to produce an acceptable and less expensive RFID antenna that is functionally similar to one made from a copper or aluminum metal foil or wire. The refinement of a printed antenna is perceived as the first step in producing a totally printed RFID tag.

Interpretation of Results: Most of the respondents (52%) report that printed RFID antennas will be prevalent in as few as three to five years, and a majority (90%) report that printed antennas will be commonplace in fifteen or fewer years. From these responses it appears that there is a strong belief that printed antennas will replace more expensive wire and foil antennas in less than fifteen years.

Survey Question 5: A totally printed passive RFID tag is likely to be available in mass quantities in:

3–5 years	15
6–10 years	16
11–15 years	12
16–20 years	3
21 or more years	3
Never	2
No Response	1

Question Rationale: The printing process, whether defined in conventional terms or in the parlance of scientists and engineers, enables the patterning of circuits that compose RFID tags and other electronic devices. Printed electronics is believed to be the process that will open the door to a new generation of inexpensive, mass-produced devices that will usher in the "Internet of Things," a world in which the items in our environment contain some level of intelligence.

Interpretation of Results: A strong majority (96%) of respondents report that it will be possible to produce a totally printed passive RFID tag, although it may take more than twenty-one years to do so. 90% believe that that task can be accomplished in twenty or fewer years, and 60% believe that it will be possible in ten or fewer years. It appears that there is a very strong agreement that printing, in some form, will provide the means to make truly low-cost RFID tags a reality.

Survey Question 6: The printing method that is most likely to make low-cost RFID tags possible is:

Lithography	6
Gravure	5
Flexography	9
Inkjet	14
Screen Printing	4
Xerography	1
Other	9
No Response	4

Question Rationale: The distinct characteristics of common printing processes may provide particular advantages in the production of RFID tag construction. For example, the heavy printable ink film thickness of screen printing may be recognized as more important than the extended run length that is obtainable using gravure, or neither may be considered as important as the smallest critical dimension that can be printed using inkjet.

Interpretation of Results: The printing process that received the strongest response (27%) is inkjet. This may be because it is the only printing process that was presented that has a common, although not necessarily equal, form, both in the commercial and scientific worlds. Regardless, inkjet has a reputation in both worlds for producing the smallest features but generally at speeds slower than other printing methods.

Survey Question 7: The production of printed RFID tags will likely be done by established commercial printers.

Strongly Agree	5
Agree	21
No Opinion	10
Disagree	10
Strongly Disagree	4
No Response	2

Question Rationale: This question assumes that RFID tags will be printed and asks if the printing manufacture will be done by those who presently produce ink-on-paper products.

Interpretation of Results: Half of the respondents (50%) express agreement that commercial printers will be charged with the task of printing RFID tags. A little more than a quarter (27%) disagree, and a little less than a quarter (23%) have either no opinion or failed to respond.

Survey Question 8: It will be possible to print RFID tags on late-model commercial printing presses.

Strongly Agree	1
Agree	18
No Opinion	17
Disagree	14
Strongly Disagree	1
No Response	1

Question Rationale: This question addresses the fitness of contemporary commercial printing presses to incorporate the necessary qualities that will enable the printing of RFID tags. Such qualities would likely include the capability to print ultra-fine features, to maintain hairline registration, and to sustain an accurate and reliable pressrun.

Interpretation of Results: The results put the population into three fairly equal groups: those who agree with the statement (37%), those who have no opinion (33%), and those who disagree or did not respond (30%).

Survey Question 9: Printed RFID tags will likely be produced in-line as part of package printing.

Strongly Agree	12
Agree	29
No Opinion	4
Disagree	6
Strongly Disagree	0
No Response	1

Question Rationale: Even if RFID tags are produced through the application of commercial printing technology, there is the question of how the tags will be applied to the items which they will identify. There is speculation that the production of the tags will occur in specialized facilities and then shipped to the point of manufacture for application at the time of packaging. There is also speculation that the tags will be embedded in the cardboard boxes or printed on the inner or outer surface that forms the main packaging material.

Interpretation of Results: A strong majority (79%) of respondents agree that printed RFID tags are likely to be produced when the package is printed. This expectation has implications for package printers who are likely to be asked by their customers to fulfill this need for them.

Survey Question 10: The mass production of printed RFID tags will require a set of skills that is presently found in the commercial printing industry.

Strongly Agree	1
Agree	20
No Opinion	10
Disagree	16
Strongly Disagree	4
No Response	1

Question Rationale: In order for commercial printers to undertake an entirely new product, i.e., printed electronics, they will need to be proficient with the use of new materials and processes and understand how to control and test their output. Whether or not this expertise exists, this question asks if the commercial printing industry is perceived to have the necessary skills to produce RFID tags.

Interpretation of Results: 40% of respondents agree (or strongly agree) that the expertise to produce printed RFID tags resides in the commercial printing industry. A significant number (21%) simply don't have an opinion or did not respond, while 38% disagree with the statement. There is no clear-cut agreement as to how the printing industry skill set will be applied.

Survey Question 11: RFID tags are likely to replace UPC bar codes on the majority of consumer goods.

Strongly Agree	15
Agree	20
No Opinion	4
Disagree	10
Strongly Disagree	2
No Response	1

Question Rationale: This question is a restatement of question 1 (RFID tags are likely to replace UPC bar codes on the majority of consumer goods in…), asking *if*, rather than *when*. Although RFID has been applied in several successful applications, over many years, its ultimate application will be in adding intelligence and value to the supply chain of goods from their point of manufacture to their point of consumption.

Interpretation of Results: A majority of respondents (67%) agree, or strongly agree, that RFID tags will be the successor to UPC bar codes.

Survey Question 12: The totally automated supermarket checkout, enabled by RFID technology, will become a reality in:

3–5 years	6
6–10 years	15
11–15 years	18
16–20 years	6
21 or more years	3
Never No	3
Response	1

Question Rationale: The ultimate goal of the automatic identification of goods movement is to have total sensing of shopping cart contents, without human intervention, upon exiting the store. The scenario would begin with the shopper entering the store and selecting a cart. Carts would have built-in bag holders, into which the customer would place their choice of empty paper or plastic bags. As the shopper selected their purchases they would place them directly into the open bags. When the customer finished shopping they would exit the store through an RFID reader portal. At that point their total would be tallied. The customer would be presented with the total and could present any coupons, also printed with RFID tags, to be scanned. To approve the total the user would press their thumb against a fingerprint scanner at which time the total would be charged to the customer's charge card, which also contains an RFID tag. They would have the option of having the receipt stored in their charge card or printed out. The customer would then exit the store, not having talked to a cashier or bagger.

Interpretation of Results: The majority (87%) of respondents believe that the automated supermarket will become a reality in twenty or fewer years. Of that majority, most respondents predict that it will occur in the time-frame of 11–15 years (35%). Only 6% of the respondents think that the totally automated shopping experience will never occur.

Comments from the Expert Group:

- Diversified paper and printing companies—e.g., Dai Nippon Mead Westvaco—may be particularly well placed if they can assimilate skills from their various divisions into a single research and business unit. Finland may be another source of innovation given their local skills in both paper and wireless technology.

- Testbeds with inkjet deposition of materials; work being done cooperatively between ink suppliers and equipment providers; concepts being pursued by companies like Plastic Logic.

- We already print antennas via flexo. We also possess de-lamination re-lamination equipment enabling the insertion of RFID tags and are actively selling this capacity. We believe label printers will print RFID labels and carton printers will print and insert RFID tags into cartons although this will take longer to achieve

- Five years ago I worked on children's books that included simple circuits printed by sheetfed lithography using electroconductive inks. I'm not sure how complex the RFID circuit is but I would envision these circuits being printed using conventional methods.

- Have used commercial screen printing for electronic circuits of electrochromic displays. High conductivity inks with high speed printing processes will be req'd. Dry/heat capacity on commercial lines will need to be increased.

- The focus I've seen in this nascent industry today is on development of technology. There appears to be little thought focused on development of the infrastructure to support production of such tags. Experimentals and [sic] underestimated the electromagnetic field effect because customers are slow to accept emerging technologies any printer that is created to print RFID at the DC will have to be smart enough to place the RFID tag on the label or leave it off based on customer requirements. Also because the apparel industry has major suppliers in countries that struggle to have telephones, the printing solution has to be portable to remote locations that could be accessed via Internet.

- Good luck! It would be interesting to see how different industries see this emerging technology working within their processes (i.e., Automatice [sic] Tier 1 automotive supplier, government, medical, apparel, food, etc...)

- This development is still very young. It is not clear yet if sufficient requirements can be met at all. The technology however is very promising.

- The RFID standard coming out this year will most likely specify a transponder type technology. This excludes printed RFID for about 20 years.

- Current methods are costly for small runs; printed antenna appears to be key; usage for product returns and reverse-logistics applications may benefit significantly from RFID; postage stamps as we know it will change too...FedEx and UPS will be on-board before long and after US Postal Service. We specialise [sic] in modifying and training operatives to produce modified printing presses (silk screen) and designing and new equipment we have designed a machine capable of producing 2illion [sic] Tags per day working on a new INKpower jet printing process we also develop the consuctive [sic] compounds required to produce RFID smart

cards on various substrates from polyester to paper.

- Most equipment can be modified to produce low quantity tag for high volumes you will need custom modified/built equipment.

- RFID has a greater potential to escalate commerce than any other innovation created to date including the creation of the credit card. Once RFID becomes pervasive automated e-commerce will become a reality and a way of life.

- It's too early to comment...

- Printed antenna's [sic] are available today the bigger problem is chip attachment is readily available today.

- As an employee in an industrial laundry company we are already working with RFID takes [sic] as well as bar codes and I see big opportunities to use them in the identification of workwear and linen.

- When I studied at the university of Rochester I was not aware of this kind of research otherwise I would have tried to make a contact and exchange experiences.

- No experience in this area I do feel that the perfection of commercial printing processes for RFID production is essential for low cost RFID tags and will be an important development in managing high volume circulation in public libraries.

- Rather than creating a new group to deliver RFID tags there is already an industry dealing with customer packaging printing requirements. Hence the introduction of this technology is "similarly" to upgrading their infrastructure install base.

Survey of the Future for RFID Tagging

The Printing Industry Center at Rochester Institute of Technology is conducting research into RFID technology and its opportunities for the printing industry. Your participation is greatly appreciated.

OPTIONAL: If you would like to receive a copy of the final report due in 2004, please enter your name and e-mail address here:

NAME

E-MAIL

Please check one box per question.

1. RFID tags are likely to replace UPC bar codes on the majority of consumer goods in...

☐ 3-5 years ☐ 6-10 years ☐ 11-15 years ☐ 16-20 years ☐ 21 or more years ☐ Never

2. In order for RFID tags to become prevalent on consumer goods, their total cost of production must be:

☐ Less than 10 cents ☐ Less than 5 cents ☐ Less than 1 cent

3. Silicon chip-based RFID tags will remain the primary form of tag production for:

☐ 3-5 years ☐ 6-10 years ☐ 11-15 years ☐ 16-20 years ☐ 21 or more years

4. Printed RFID antennas (used with a silicon–based RFID chip) will be the primary antenna format in:

☐ 3-5 years ☐ 6-10 years ☐ 11-15 years ☐ 16-20 years ☐ 21 or more years ☐ Never

5. A totally printed passive RFID tag is likely to be available in mass quantities in:

☐ 3-5 years ☐ 6-10 years ☐ 11-15 years ☐ 16-20 years ☐ 21 or more years ☐ Never

6. The printing method that is most likely to make low-cost RFID tags possible is:

☐ Lithography ☐ Gravure ☐ Flexography ☐ Inkjet ☐ Screen Printing ☐ Xerography ☐ Other

7. The production of printed RFID tags will likely be done by established commercial printers.

☐ Strongly Agree ☐ Agree ☐ No Opinion ☐ Disagree ☐ Strongly Disagree

8. It will be possible to print RFID tags on late model commercial printing presses.

☐ Strongly Agree ☐ Agree ☐ No Opinion ☐ Disagree ☐ Strongly Disagree

9. Printed RFID tags will likely be produced in-line as part of package printing.

☐ Strongly Agree ☐ Agree ☐ No Opinion ☐ Disagree ☐ Strongly Disagree

10. The mass production of printed RFID tags will require a set of skills that is presently found in the commercial printing industry.

☐ Strongly Agree ☐ Agree ☐ No Opinion ☐ Disagree ☐ Strongly Disagree

11. RFID tags are likely to replace UPC bar codes on the majority of consumer goods.

☐ Strongly Agree ☐ Agree ☐ No Opinion ☐ Disagree ☐ Strongly Disagree

12. The totally automated supermarket checkout, enabled by RFID technology, will become a reality in:

☐ 3-5 years ☐ 6-10 years ☐ 11-15 years ☐ 16-20 years ☐ 21 or more years ☐ Never

COMMENTS: What are your opinions and experiences regarding the use of commercial printing processes for the production of electronic devices, such as RFID tags? (Extensive input may be e-mailed to mlkppr@rit.edu.)

Return of Form: You may return this form as an e-mail attachment to Michael Kleper, mlkppr@rit.edu, or you may print it and fax it to Michael Kleper, 585 475-7087, or mail it to: Professor Michael Kleper, Rochester Institute of Technology, School of Print Media, 69 Lomb Memorial Drive, Rochester, NY 14623.

R·I·T Printing Industry Center

ENDNOTES

1. The term *polymer electronics* is sometimes referred to as *solution-based electronics*. *Small molecule display technology* is sometimes referred to as being *vapor-based*. The distinction between solution-based vs. vapor-based has simplified the manner by which people can refer to polymer vs. small molecule OLED manufacture.

2. Yoshida, 2003.

3. Miller, 2002, p. 10.

4. Lawrence, 2003.

5. The information consumer may print what they view locally on a desktop or networked printer; however, the significance is that the information was not delivered to them in printed form from a commercial source.

6. Comdex, November 2002; 2nd Advanced Technology Workshop on Printing an Intelligent Future, March 2003; Smart Labels USA, March 2003; Society for Information Display (SID), May 2003.

7. NACS Online Staff, 2003. NACS is the National Association of Convenience Stores.

8. Auto-ID may be applied to objects (bar codes, radio frequency identification) and to people (voice recognition, electronic signature capture, and biometrics). The use of RFID tagging for tracking people through the implantation of a microchip under the skin, or the attachment of a secure bracelet or anklet, has been used for confining prisoners and restricting personnel access to high-security areas. Sub-dermal tagging, a controversial subject, has been discussed for tracking suspected terrorists and controlling the wandering of dementia patients.

9. Uniform Code Council, 2002.

10. Bernard Silver died in 1962 at the age of thirty-eight.

11. Hagey, 1998.

12. Bonsor, 2002.

13. Auto-ID technology has been recognized as a legitimate field of study. Automated Identification & Data Capture (AIDC) is a sensor-based engineering field taught at many universities including MIT, Ohio State, and Purdue.

14. Lasco Fittings, 2002.

15. Code 39 was adopted by the U.S. Department of Defense on September 1, 1981, for marking all products sold to the United States military.

16. Uniform Code Council, Inc., Princeton Pike Corporate Center, 1009 Lenox Drive, Suite 202, Lawrenceville, NJ 08648, phone: 609/620-0200, fax: 609/620-1200, email: info@uc-council.org.

17. Haberman, Alan L., Editor. *Twenty-five Years Behind Bars.* Cambridge, MA: Harvard University Press, 2001, p. 143.

18. Personal correspondence with George Laurer, May 3, 2003.

19. Much of the early work on educating the printing industry on the proper printing of UPC was done at Rochester Institute of Technology. It may also be incumbent on RIT to educate the industry on the likely successor to the UPC bar code process, RFID.

20. Uniform Code Council, Inc., Princeton Pike Corporate Center, 1009 Lenox Drive, Suite 202, Lawrenceville, NJ 08648, phone: 609/620-0200, web: http://www.uc-council.org.

21. Personal correspondence with George Laurer, May 3, 2003.

22. Sarma, 2001, p. 15.

23. Smart ID Technology PTE LTD, 2003, http://www.smartid.com.sg/RFID.htm.

24. *RFID Journal* Staff, 2003.

25. Kevin Ashton, founder and executive director of the MIT Auto-ID Center.

26. According to Gerry Meyer of Proctor & Gamble, approximately 7–9% of all world trade is composed of counterfeit products. This is equal to about $500 billion, of which about $255 million is sales lost by Proctor & Gamble. It cannot be calculated how much inferior counterfeit products cost a company in damage to their brand and consumer goodwill.

27. IDTechEX Limited, 2003. It should be noted that virtually all products presently contain UPC bar

codes, amounting to trillions of items. There will likely be a transitional period wherein items will contain both a UPC bar code and an RFID tag.

28. IDTechEX Limited, 2003, p. 14.

29. ThingMagic LLC, One Broadway, Cambridge, MA 02142, phone: 617/758-4136 or 4135, ffax: 707/215-0156, email: info@thingmagic.com, web: http://www.thingmagic.com.

30. The fabrication of an RFID tag consists of four operations. First is the creation of the IC chip, second is the creation of the antenna, third is the assembly of the chip to the antenna, and fourth is the fabrication of the chip/antenna assembly to a carrier, such as paper. When the chip is attached to the antenna it is necessary to make proper contact, and in exactly the right places. This is done robotically and using a wire-bonding method called "flip chip" which simplifies its connection. Flip chip involves the application of a conductive adhesive to connect the chip's electrodes to the antenna.

31. Le, 1997.

32. The Japan-based RFID standards group, uID (ubiquitous ID) Center, has developed an alternative standard that it is presenting for global consideration.

33. IDTechEX Limited, 2003.

34. Sarma, 2001, p. 6.

35. Sarma, 2001, p. 5.

36. Sarma, 2001, p. 12.

37. Koninklijke Philips Electronics N.V., 2002.

38. Webmaster, 2003.

39. *RFID Journal* Staff, 2003.

40. The governing bodies which regulate allowable power levels are the Federal Communications Commission (FCC) in the United States, the European Telecommunications Standards Institute (ETSI) in Europe, and the Ministry for Post and Telecommunications (MPT) in Japan.

41. Common frequencies in use in the United States are:

AM radio	535 kHz to 1.7 Mhz
FM radio	88 MHz to 108 MHz
Garage door opener	~40 MHz
Radio-controlled cars	~75 MHz
GPS	1227 to 1575 MHz

42. Koninklijke Philips Electronics N.V., 2002.

43. *RFID Journal* Staff, 2003. Although Toppan will be producing the T-Junction chip, it was invented by Telemidic of Japan. Toppan has secured exclusive manufacturing and sales rights.

44. Sorrells, 2002.

45. Sarma, 2001.

46. InformationWeek.com Staff, 2001.

47. Alien Technology Corporation, 18220 Butterfield Blvd., Morgan Hill, CA 95037, phone: 408/782-3900, fax: 408/782-3910, email: info@alientechnology.com, web: http://www.AlienTechnology.com.

48. Heyman and Florkemeier, 2002. "Up to 20% of goods get lost between supplier and store." Slide 10.

49. Alien Technology Corporation, 1999.

50. The variety of materials that can be used to produce Nanoblocks includes silicon, silicon-germanium, gallium arsenide, indium gallium phosphide, and others. Sanjay Sarma, director of MIT's Auto-ID Center, estimates the cost of a typical wafer at between $500 to $1000.

51. The Nanoblock production, which consists of etching, shaping, and freeing the chips from the wafer, is a proprietary patent-pending process.

52. Quoted from personal correspondence, July 1, 2003.

53. Alien Technology Corporation, 1999.

54. Quoted from personal correspondence, July 1, 2003.

55. IDTechEX Limited, 2003.

56. IFPMA, International Federation of Pharmaceutical Manufacturers Associations, 30 rue de St-Jean, P.O. Box 9, 1211 Geneva 18, Switzerland, phone: +41 (22) 340 1200, fax: +41 (22) 340 1380, email: admin@ifpma.org, web: http://www.ifpma.org. And The International Conference on Harmonisation of Technical Requirements for Registration of Pharmaceuticals for Human Use, http://www.ich.org/.

57. Das, 2002, p. 7.

58. Shimmin, 2003, p. 40.

59. Shimmin, 2003, pp. 42–44.

60. Mullins, 2003, p. 8D.

61. *RFID Journal* Staff, 2003.

62. Philips Electronics, Mobile Display Systems, Components Division, 1000 West Maude Avenue, Sunnyvale, CA 94085-2810, phone: 845/246-2811, web: http://www.philips.com.

63. http://www.ibiblio.org/lunarbin/worldpop.

64. http://www.destronfearing.com. There are also more than 200 million domestic pets on this planet.

65. Destron Fearing Corporation, 490 Villaume Ave., South St. Paul, MN 55075-2445, web: http://www.destronfearing.com.

66. IDTechEX Limited, 2003.

67. The MIT Auto-ID Center, 77 Massachusetts Ave., Bldg. 3-449, Cambridge, MA 02139-4307, web: http://www.autoidcenter.org. The more than 35 industry members (end-users), which include International Paper, Gillette, Wal-Mart, and Proctor & Gamble, each paid $300,000 to join, while vendors pay $150,000 for a three-year period.

68. NACS Online Staff, 2002.

69. Ironically, in 1987 Kmart of Canada made news by telling its suppliers that it would not sell their goods if they did not contain a UPC bar code.

70. *RFID Journal* Staff, 2003.

71. Shim, 2003.

72. Schoenberger, 2002.

73. Vijayan and Brewin, 2003.

74. Shim, 2003.

75. Gilbert and Shim, 2003. On July 9, 2003, Wal-Mart unexpectedly announced that it was withdrawing from a joint technology demonstration of smart shelving that it had agreed to conduct with Gillette at a store in Brockton, MA.

76. Albano and Engels, 2002.

77. Albrecht. 2002. The observation is based on videos titled *Home of the Future* and *Store of the Future*.

78. Johnson, 2003.

79. *RFID Journal* Staff, 2003

80. The announcement on March 11 was issued by Philips Semiconductor stating that it would ship 15 million RFID tags to Benetton for use in its Sisley clothing line. Benetton stated on April 4 that it has only purchased 200 RFID tags to date and was only researching their use.

81. Chiesa, Genz, et. al, 2002, p. 34.

82. Das, 2002, p. 11.

83. Das, 2002, p. 8.

84. Caterinicchia, 2003.

85. Heyman and Florkemeier, 2002, slide 10.

86. Editor, 2001.

87. Chiesa, Genz, et. al, 2002, p. 24.

88. INKODE USA, 8230 Old Courthouse Road, Vienna, VA 22182, phone: 703/276-8000, fax: 703/903-0332, email: USA@inkode.com, web: http://www.inkode.com.

89. Brollier, 2003. The author classifies print quality in four areas: film thickness, variation in film thickness, feature size, and color-to-color relationships.

90. Hitachi has a version of its μ-Chip with a self-contained antenna. See page 19.

91. Subramanian, 2003.

92. Graciela B. Blanchet, Yueh-Lin Loo, et. al, 2002.

93. Email from Franz Sigg, July 3, 2003.

94. Whitmore, Schake, et. al, 2003.

95. Miller, 2002, p. 11.

96. Whitesides has identified the following printing techniques comprising the field of soft lithography: Near-Field Phase Shift Lithography, Replica Molding, Micromolding in Capillaries (MIMIC), Microtransfer Molding™, Solvent-assisted Microcontact Molding (SAMIM), and Microcontact Printing (CP).

97. Stix, 2002.

98. Service, 1997.

99. Whitesides, 1997.

100. Here is a good explanation of transistor construction, which is the basis for IC fabrication: "Complementary metal-oxide semiconductor (CMOS) is the technology commonly used to fabricate transistors. Semiconductors are exactly what the name implies. The crystalline materials, including silicon and germanium, aren't as good as, say, copper wire in allowing electrons to flow through. But they're not that bad at it either. Also, impurities such as boron can be added to the semiconductor to selectively enhance its conductivity. This process, called doping, results in a semiconductor with either an abundance of mobile positive charge (a p-type material) or an abundance of mobile negative charge (an n-type material).

The transistor itself contains three terminals: the source, the gate, and the drain. In the most common transistor type, the source and the drain, doped n-type, reside in a p-type body. The conductivity of the p-type region between the source and drain is controlled by the gate, which is located directly above the channel with a thin interposing oxide layer. This layer is needed to prevent electrical current from flowing between the gate and the channel. The size of a transistor actually refers to the length of the gate, which corresponds to the spacing between the source and the drain. Applying a positive voltage to the gate attracts the negatively charged electrons from the source into a surface channel, creating a continuous n-type layer for current to flow between the source and drain. At this point, the transistor is on. If the voltage at the gate is removed, the n-type channel layer cannot be maintained, switching the transistor off." Pescovitz, 2002,

101. Oren, 1998.

102. Kolb, 2001.

103. Williams, 1998.

104. Nakamura, 2003.

105. Calvert, 2001.

106. Shimoda, 2003.

107. Brazis and Daniel R. Gamota, 2003.

108. Lawrence, 2003.

109. Flint Ink, 4600 Arrowhead Drive, Ann Arbor, MI 48105, phone: 734/622-6000, web: http://www.flintink.com.

110. Flint Ink business partners include R.T. Circuits, Saltcoats, Scotland; Auto-ID Center, Boston, MA; MIT, Boston, MA; University of Michigan, Ann Arbor, MI; Parelec, Rocky Hill, NJ; and Advanced Conductive Materials, Atascadero, CA.

111. Lawrence, 2003.

112. Parelec Inc., 5 Crescent Avenue, Building C, P.O. Box 236, Rocky Hill, NJ 08553-0236, phone: 609/279-0072, web: http://www.parelec.com.

113. Acheson Colloids Company, 1600 Washington Avenue, Port Huron, MI 48060, phone: 800/255-1908, fax: 810/984-1446, email: web.mail@nstarch.com, web: http://www.achesonindustries.com.

114. COMMOTION Printed Display Solutions, The Dow Chemical Company, 1702 Building, Midland, MI 48674, phone: 989/636-9890.

115. Hebbar, 2001. Sun Computer's chief technology officer Greg Papadopoulos predicts that the Internet will pass through three phases. The first is the Internet of computers (108), composed of things that we use, such as desktop computers, where we are now (2001–2003). Next comes the Internet of things that embed computers, composed of things that we work around us, such as cell phones, PDAs, TVs, and cars (1011) (1998–2004), and

ultimately there will be the Internet of things which will incorporate micro-electronic machines (MEMs), composed of things we wear and interact with, such as clothes, thermostats, switches, etc. (1014) (2004–2007).

116. Plastic Logic, 34 Cambridge Science Park, Milton Road, Cambridge CB4 0FX UK, phone: +44 (0) 1223 706010, web: www.plasticlogic.com.

117. Email to author on July 10, 2003.

118. Crosslink™ Polymer Research, 950 Bolger Court, St. Louis, MO 63026, phone: 877/456-5864, 636 349-0050, fax: 636/349-0003, email: contactus@crosslinkresearch.com, web: http://www.crosslinkresearch.com.

119. The lifetime of the light emission system is defined as 50% of original brightness. This standard applies to the estimated life expectancy of virtually all displays.

120. http://www.paperplusplus.net/. As displayed on the Paper++ website: "Paper++ is a collaboration of Kings College London, HP Laboratories Bristol, ETH Zurich, Anitra, and Arjo Wiggins. The project is part of the European initiative The Disappearing Computer, and is funded in part by the Commission of the European Union, and by the Swiss Federal Office for Education and Science."

121. http://www.agfa.com/sfc/polymer/.

122. Acreo AB, Electrum 236, SE-164 40 Kista, Sweden, phone: +46 8 632 77 00, fax: +46 8 750 54 30, web: www.paella.acreo.se.

123. Das, 2002, p. 14.

124. Power Paper, POB 12, Kibbutz Einat, Israel 49910, phone: 972/390-7500, email: info@ powerpaper.com, web: www.powerpaper.com.

125. Quoted from a document titled "PowerID™ Description.doc," provided to the author by the company.

126. The first U.S. licensee, Graphic Solutions, Inc., http://www.graphicsolutionsinc.com, was announced on April 30, 2003.

127. Technology can enable capabilities that challenge the notion of what it is to be human. Looking out fifty years or more into the future, low-cost, nano-level technology may enable the addition of a sixth human sense. Either through implantation or the use of a wearable device, people will be capable of sensing and reading digital data directly from stored or ambient sources, with the functions common to today's personal computers. Human-enabled data recognition and processing will make computer data visible directly, whether it is image-, sound-, touch-, smell-, taste-, or motion-based.

REFERENCES

Albano, S. and D.W. Engels. 2002. Auto-ID Center Field Trial: Phase I Summary. Cambridge, MA: MIT.

Albrecht, K. 2002. "Supermarket Cards: The Tip of the Retail Surveillance Iceberg." *Denver University Law Review* 79(4): 534–539, 558–565.

Alien Technology Corporation. 1999. Alien Technology Corporation White Paper: Fluidic Self Assembly. Morgan Hill, CA.

Blanchet, Graciela B., Yueh-Lin Loo, et. al. 2002. "Large area, high resolution, dry printing of conducting polymers for organic electronics." *Applied Physics Letters* 82 (3): 463–465.

Bonsor, K. 2002. How Smart Labels Will Work. howstuffworks, 2003.

Brazis, P.W., Jr. and Daniel R. Gamota. 2003. "IEEE Standardization for Printed Electronics: An Overview of Recent Working Group Activities." *IMAPS Printing an Intelligent Future:* Boston, MA: International Microelectronics and Packaging Society.

Brollier, B. 2003. "Print Characteristics for Graphics vs. Electronics." *IMAPS Printing an Intelligent Future.* Boston, MA: International Microelectronics and Packaging Society.

Calvert, P. 2001. "Inkjet Printing for Materials and Devices." *Chem. Mater.* (American Chemical Society) 13: 3299–3305.

Caterinicchia, D. 2003. "'Quantum leap' in Wartime Logistics." *Federal Computer Week.*

Chiesa, M., R. Genz, et. al. 2002. RFID: A week long survey on the technology and its potential. Ivrea, Italy: Interaction Design Institute Ivrea.

Das, R. 2002. "The Benefits and Future of Smart Packaging." *Smart Packaging Journal* 1(1): 2–15.

Editor. 2001. "Bullish RFID Market Projected as Data Capture Demand Grows; Smart Labels Seen as Key

Link in Tomorrow's Industrial Sector." *Supply Chain Systems Magazine.* 2003.

Gilbert, A. and R. Shim. 2003. Wal-Mart cancels 'smart shelf' trial. cnet news.com.

Hagey, W. 1998. *The History of Bar Codes.* 2003.

Hebbar, P. 2001. Connect to a smarter world, courtesy [of] Sun, CIOL Enterprise Connect. 2003.

Heyman, D. and C. Florkemeier. 2002. The New Network: Smart Objects, Smarter Companies. Cambridge, MA: MIT Auto-ID Center.

IDTechEX Limited. 2003. "Broader Applications for RFID Cards." *Smart Labels Analyst* (25): 1–23.

———. 2003. "RFID for logistics—10 business opportunities for the New Year." *Smart Labels Analyst* (24): 1–6.

InformationWeek.com Staff. 2001. The Fast Track. InformationWeek.com. 2003.

Johnson, B. 2003. "CASPIAN Founder Takes Strong Public Stand Against RFID." *The Voice of Freedom.*

Kolb, R. 2001. EUV Lithography Making Possible Next Generation of Semiconductors. Berkeley Lab. 2003.

Koninklijke Philips Electronics N.V. 2002. Smart labels. 2003.

———. 2002. Tuning to the right frequency. 2003.

Lasco Fittings. 2002. *History of Bar Codes.* 2003.

Lawrence, D. 2003. Flint Ink's Conductive Inks Product Update. Ann Arbor, MI: Flint Ink.

———. 2003. "Test Methods for Printing Inks in Electronic Structures." *IMAPS Printing an Intelligent Future.* Boston, MA: International Microelectronics And Packaging Society.

Le, R. 1997. "Radio Frequency Tags: An Alternative to Bar Coding." *Logistics Spectrum.* 2003.

Michel, B., A. Bernard, et. al. 2001. "Printing meets lithography: Soft approaches to high-resolution patterning." *IBM Journal of Research and Development* 45, No. 5.

Miller, F. 2002. "Polytronics: Rolling out the chips." *Fraunhofer Magazine:* 8–12.

Mullins, R. 2003. Printing: "The future is now." *Rochester Democrat and Chronicle.* Rochester, NY: 12D, 8D.

NACS Online Staff. 2002. Wal-Mart RFID Test Enters Phase Two. NACS Online. 2003.

———. The Internet of Things. NACS Online. 2003.

Nakamura, R. 2003. "Printing for Organic Electronics." *IMAPS Printing an Intelligent Future.* Boston, MA: International Microelectronics and Packaging Society.

Oren, T. 1998. *Ten More Years of Torrid Infotech Growth.* Menlo Park, CA: Institute for the Future.

Pescovitz, D. 2002. Berkeley breathes new life into silicon: Nanotransistors could hold Moore's Law at bay for decades. Forefront: College of Engineering, University of California, Berkeley. 2003.

RFID Journal Staff. 2003. "Benetton Explains RFID Privacy Flap." *RFID Journal.*

———. 2003. "Genesis of the Versatile RFID Tag." *RFID Journal.*

———. 2003. "RSA Security Designs RFID Blocker." *RFID Journal.*

———. 2003. "Three French companies are offering 'Intelligent Film for Identification,' which could make forging passports much more difficult." *RFID Journal.*

———. 2003. "Toppan Gears Up for Low-Cost RFID." *RFID Journal.*

———. 2003. "Wal-Mart Draws Line in the Sand." *RFID Journal.*

Sarma, S. 2001. White Paper: Towards the 5¢ Tag. Cambridge, MA: MIT.

Schoenberger, C.R. 2002. The Internet of Things. Forbes.com. 2003.

Service, R.F. 1997. "Patterning Electronics on the Cheap." *Science.* 278: 383–384.

Shim, R. 2003. Wal-Mart to throw its weight behind RFID. CNet News.Com.

Shimmin, R. 2003. "Intelligent Labels." *Labels & Labelling.* 25: 40, 42–44, 46.

Shimoda, T. 2003. Ink-jet Technology for Fabrication Processes of Flat Panel Displays. Baltimore, MD: Society for Information Display.

Smart ID Technology PTE LTD. 2003. Origin of RFID.

Sorrells, P. 2002. Optimizing read range in RFID systems. EDN.com.

Stix, G. 2002. Soft Manufacturing. ScientificAmerican.com. 2003.

Subramanian, V. 2003. "Towards Printed Low-Cost RFID Tags: Device, Materials and Circuit Technologies." *IMAPS Printing an Intelligent Future.* Boston, MA.

Uniform Code Council, I. 2002. The Origins of a Bar Code. 2003.

Vijayan, J. and B. Brewin. 2003. "Wal-Mart to deploy radio ID tags for supply tracking." *Computerworld.*

Webmaster. 2003. How Does It Work? Trovan Electronic Identification Systems.

Whitesides, G.M. 1997. Soft Lithography. R&D Status and Trends in Nanoparticles, Nanostructured Materials, and Nanodevices in the United States. Arlington, VA: Loyola University.

Whitmore, M., J. Schake, et. al. 2003. "An Overview of Screen & Stencil Printing Technology." *IMAPS Printing an Intelligent Future.* Boston, MA: International Microelectronics and Packaging Society.

Williams, R.S. 1998. Functional Nanostructures, Hewlett-Packard Laboratories. 2003.

Yoshida, J. 2003. "Europe quietly forms polymer electronics project." *Silicon Strategies.*

About the Author

Michael L. Kleper is the Paul and Louise Miller Distinguished Professor in the School of Print Media, Rochester Institute of Technology. Professor Kleper has more than thirty-five years of college teaching experience in the area of graphic communication technology, with emphasis in digital publishing and imaging, electronic prepress, cross-media publishing, and digital workflows. He is the author of eight books, and one CD-ROM, the latest of which is *The Handbook of Digital Publishing* (Prentice Hall, 2001). The two-volume handbook is the biggest and most comprehensive on the subject and has been lauded universally. In the summer of 2003 the book was translated and printed in Russian.

Since 1979 he has edited several newsletters, now online in the form of *The Kleper Report on Digital Publishing* (http://www.printerport.com/kdp). Professor Kleper has written hundreds of articles appearing in the trade press and was the recipient of the NCA Distinguished Industry Service Award and other honors. In 2001 he was named as a Fulbright Senior Specialist by the J. William Fulbright Foreign Scholarship Board (FSB), the Bureau of Education and Cultural Affairs of the Department of State (ECA), and the Council for International Exchange of Scholars (CIES). The Fulbright Senior Specialist Program sends U.S. academic experts to overseas academic institutions fortwo to six weeks to lecture, lead seminars, work with foreign coun-

terparts in the development of curriculum and course materials, and to conduct needs assessments.

Professor Kleper has been a faculty associate of the RIT Printing Industry Center, a new partnership with the Alfred P. Sloan Foundation. The center is an innovative think tank for the printing industry designed to work to increase knowledge of the complex influences that shape business enterprises, from new technologies to workforce issues, to the impact of globalization. Professor Kleper's research dealt with the generation beyond print on paper, and technologies that enrich paper with intelligence.

In May 2002, Professor Kleper was awarded the Gitner Family Prize for Outstanding Professional Achievement in Graphic Communications. The prize is awarded annually to a faculty member in the RIT College of Imaging Arts and Sciences who makes significant contributions to his or her profession.

Professor Kleper has also conducted seminars for RIT's Technical and Education Center for the Graphic Arts, and serves as a consultant to education and industry. Prior to his appointment to the Miller Chair, Professor Kleper was a senior faculty member in RIT/NTID's Digital Imaging and Publishing Technology department and the industry liaison for The NTID High Technology Center for Electronic Publishing and Imaging, a state-of-the-art laboratory for deaf students, and the thousands of industry seminar participants who visit RIT each year.

About GATF

The Graphic Arts Technical Foundation is a nonprofit, scientific, technical, and educational organization dedicated to the advancement of the graphic communications industries worldwide. Its mission is to serve the field as the leading resource for technical information and services through research and education. GATF is a partner of the Printing Industries of America (PIA), the world's largest graphic arts trade association, and its regional affiliates.

For 80 years the Foundation has developed leading-edge technologies and practices for printing. GATF's staff of researchers, educators, and technical specialists partner with nearly 14,000 corporate members in over 80 countries to help them maintain their competitive edge by increasing productivity, print quality, process control, and environmental compliance, and by implementing new techniques and technologies. Through conferences, satellite symposia, workshops, consulting, technical support, laboratory services, and publications, GATF strives to advance a global graphic communications community.

The GATF*Press* publishes books on nearly every aspect of the field; learning modules (step-by-step instruction booklets); audiovisuals (CD-ROMs and videotapes); and research and technology reports. It also publishes *GATFWorld*, a bimonthly magazine providing articles on industry technologies, trends, and practices.

For more information on GATF products and services, please visit our website at www.gain.net or write to us at 200 Deer Run Road, Sewickley, PA 15143-2600 (phone: 412/741-6860)

About PIA

In continuous operation since 1887 and headquartered in Alexandria, Virginia, Printing Industries of America, Inc. (PIA), is the world's largest graphic arts trade association representing an industry with more than 1 million employees and $156 billion in sales annually.

PIA promotes the interests of over 14,000 member companies. Companies become members in PIA by joining one of 28 regional affiliate organizations throughout the United States or by joining the Canadian Printing Industries Association. International companies outside North America may join PIA directly.

Printing Industries of America, Inc. is in the business of promoting programs, services, and an environment that helps its members operate profitably. Many of PIA's members are commercial printers, allied graphic arts firms such as electronic imaging companies, equipment manufacturers, and suppliers.

PIA has developed several special industry groups, sections, and councils to meet the unique needs of specific market segments. Each group provides members with current information on their specific market and helps members stay ahead of the competition.

PIA's special industry groups are the Web Offset Association (WOA), Graphic Arts Marketing Information Service (GAMIS), Label Printing Industries of America (LPIA), and Binding Industries of America International (BIA).

The special sections and councils include Printing Industry Financial Executives (PIFE), Sales & Marketing Executives (S&ME), Electronic Prepress Section (EPS), Digital Printing Council (DPC), and the E-Business Council (EBC).

PIA also publishes *Management Portfolio*, a bimonthly magazine that provides information on business management practices for printers; economic trends, benchmarks, and forecasts; legislative and regulatory affairs; human and industrial relations issues; sales, marketing, and customer service techniques; and management resources.

For more detailed information on PIA products and services, please visit PIA at www.gain.net or write 100 Daingerfield Road, Alexandria, VA 22314 (phone: 703/519-8100).